1. The weather is _gorgeous_.
   Everyone wants to _go out_.
   Nobody wants to _stay in_.

   gorgeous ⑩ 非常漂亮的 ⑩ 極好的

   The weather is { perfect.
   天氣很棒。   { wonderful.
                { very nice.

She is _gorgeous_. 她很漂亮。
Your dress is _gorgeous_.
   你的衣服很漂亮。
The view is gorgeous.
   這裡的景色很漂亮。

go out 出去玩 (= go outside)
stay in 待在家裡
= stay indoors
= stay in the house

We have been shopping for
   a while.
My feet are _sore_.
My patience is _running_
   out. 我快沒有耐心了。

a while 一段時間
quite a while 很長一段時間
My feet are { sore.
             { aching.
             { killing me.
= My feet hurt. 我的腳很痛。
= I have sore feet.

run out 用完；耗盡
My time is _running out_.
My money is _running out_.
My energy is _running out_.

You can _go walk around_
   你可以四處走走。
I'm going to _hang out_
   here.
I will wait _until_ you
   come back.

You can _go_ (and) _walk around_.
        "
       (to)
        ✗
= You can go walking around.
   hang out here 待在這裡
= hang around here
= stay here
I will wait _until_ you come
   back.
= I will wait for you to
   return.

= I will b⋯⋯⋯⋯⋯ or

                              e.
                              me.

I'm not at all _used to_
being treated like that.
我一點也不習慣被那樣
對待。

She is very stubborn. 頑固的
She is narrow-minded
She never listens to me.
narrow-minded 心胸狹窄的
open-minded 心胸寬大的

She has a terrible personality.
She isn't satisfied with anything.
Nobody likes being around her.

Nobody likes being around her.
沒有人喜歡和她在一起。
= Nobody likes to be around her.
= Nobody wants to hang out with her.
恐佈的個性。
* He is not a man of his word.
(他不遵守諾言。)
He is not responsible. (他沒有責任感。)

---

3. Everyone is present except Tom.
He hasn't arrived yet.
He might not be able to catch up with us.

他可能無法趕上我們。
catch up with 趕上；追上
在此 might = may。
He hasn't come yet. [正，少用]

I've been here an hour.
It seems like forever
I don't feel like waiting any longer. 我不想再等了。

It seems like forever.
似乎好像很久了。
= It seems like a long time.
[It 指時間]
feel like + V-ing 想要

I was a little upset.
He arrived very late.
I was made to wait for a long time.
我被迫等很久。
主動: He made me wait for a long time.
       S V O OC
被動: I was made to wait for a long time.
      S   V   SC
使役動詞改被動，要保留 to。

---

be made, be called, be elected, be named 後加主詞補語。[文法 P.14]
He is named Edward.
           主補
He is called Eddie.
          主補
He was elected president.
            主補
他被選為董事長。

P.2

4.
- I know all about that book.
- I read it before.
  (= I've read it before.)
- You should put it on your reading list.

know all about 非常了解
reading list 閱讀書單

> I know all about that movie.
> I saw it before. (= I've seen it before.)
> You should put it on your watching list.

- This novel is worth reading from cover to cover.
- It's a fascinating story.
- It's one of my favorites.

be worth + V-ing 主.及物. 無受
= be worthy of being p.p.
from cover to cover 從頭到尾
fascinating adj. ①迷人的 ②有趣的
= very interesting
favorite adj. 最喜愛的
        n. 最喜愛的人或物

- I was so absorbed in the book. 我迷上這本書。
- It was a real page-turner. 這書一看就停不下來。
- I kept reading through lunch and dinner.

[əb'zↄːrbd]75% [əb'sↄːrbd]25%

be absorbed in
  專心於；沉迷於；迷上
= be lost in

page-turner 令人欲罷不能的書

I kept reading through lunch and dinner.
我一直讀，連午餐晚餐都在讀。
[讀後語法]
= 餐各詞無冠詞。

5.
- We are buddies.
- We have done a lot together.
- We've known each other for ages.

buddy n. 朋友 [用於男生]
= pal [用於男生]   We are friends.
= friend   [都可用]
for ages 很久
= for years
= for a long time

- He is very well-paid.
- His business is booming. (他的生意興隆。)
- He is rich enough to buy anything.

He is very well-paid.
① 他的薪水很高。
  (= His salary is very high.)
② 他賺很多錢。
  (= He makes a lot of money.)

boom [bum] v.
① 發出隆隆聲
② 繁榮；迅速發展

He can barely speak English.
He had no clear-cut plan.
He was foolish to go
overseas. 他出國真是愚蠢。
= It was foolish of him to go overseas.
barely 幾乎不 (= hardly)
clear-cut 明確的 (= clear)
go overseas 出國
= go abroad

6. I have been walking for
an hour.
I haven't gotten there yet.
Are these the right
directions to get there?
到那裡的方向是正確的嗎?
= Is this the right way to
get there?
「方向」不只一個, 有轉彎, 故用
複數形 directions。

I may have lost my way.
• 我可能已經迷路了。
I think I need some
assistance.
　=help
Is there anyone to help
me out?
may have p.p. 現在推測過去
{ help me out 幫我一下忙
{ help me 幫助我; 救我

I didn't prepare well.
I didn't give it my all.
I'm deeply disappointed
with myself.

give it one's all 盡全力
be disappointed with
對~很失望

7. May I borrow a pen?
Can you lend me something
to write with?
Even a pencil will do.
就算是鉛筆也可以。
{ borrow + 受
{ lend + 間受 + 直受
even, only, not 可修飾名詞
exactly, hardly, merely
also, just, do
[文堂 p. 228]
　副　　詞

That will do. (行, 好, 可以)
That won't do. (不行。)
I sent it out today.
I registered the package.
我用掛號寄那個包裹。
By next week, she will
have received it.
= Next week, she will
receive it.

什麼是「一口氣考試英語」？

　　沒有想到，可以把考試題目變成「一口氣考試英語」，同學背完之後，會說英語，也會考試，如：

> Little _____ seeing you again here. 【駒澤大】
> (A) dream of did I　　　(B) did I dream of
> (C) I dreamed of　　　　(D) I did dream of

這條題目是考「倒裝句」，否定副詞放句首，助動詞放在主詞前面倒裝，故 (C) 和 (D) 都錯，只能選 (B)。Little 這個副詞，在助動詞前，等於 Never。Little did I dream of...，這類的文法題常考，放在「一口氣考試英語」中就更精彩了。你看看下面三句，一口氣說出來多棒！

> What a nice surprise! (真令人驚喜！)【常考】
> I can't believe my eyes.
> （我無法相信我的眼睛。）
> *Little did I dream of seeing you here.*
> （做夢也沒想到會在這裡看到你。）【駒澤大】

這三句話隨時可說，偶然見到朋友，連續說這三句，你的英語會話就無人能比了！

　　你會了 What a nice surprise! 這個句型，你就會說出：What a pleasant surprise! 和 What a wonderful surprise! 從 I can't believe my eyes. 同時學會 I can't believe it. 背的每一個句子都是一個句型，可無限延伸。同學要養成習慣，即使見到中國人，也要對他說英文。如果對中國人能說，對外國人更能說。

　　從一開口說三句，變成一開口說九句，講得快，腦筋裡就不會想到中翻英了。再看下面三句：

> What are you doing on Sunday?【帝塚山學院大】
> （你禮拜天要做什麼？）
> Come stay with us, *won't you*?【東海大】
> （來和我們一起住，好嗎？）
> Let's go hiking, *shall we*?【東洋大】
> （我們去走一走路，鍛鍊一下，好嗎？）

學英語會話，最高的境界，就是會用「句尾附加句」。問朋友禮拜天有沒有空，說：***What are you doing on Sunday?*** 比 Are you free on Sunday?（你禮拜天有空嗎？）或 Are you busy on Sunday?（你禮拜天忙嗎？）更道地、更婉轉。不會說英文，真好！可以藉學英文的機會，把口才練好。像 go hiking，美國人常說，字典上翻譯是「去健行」，與我們平常所說的話格格不入。例如，到陽明山去爬山，就是 go hiking。中文說的「爬山」，其實是在山上走，去郊外走，也是 go hiking。go mountain climbing 則是「攀登山」，使用的情況較少。

再背三句：

> You can ride a bike anywhere.
> （你可以騎腳踏車到任何地方。）
> You can rent a bike *by the hour*.
> （你可以按小時租腳踏車。）【姬路獨協大】
> There are bicycle paths all around the city.
> （整個城市都有腳踏車專用道。）

這幾句話可還用在作文中。

全書共有 6 個 Unit，每一個 Unit 有 81 句，共 486 句，我們在 2015 年 9 月 9 日至 10 月 28 日，開了「一口氣考試英語班」，效果極佳。最受益的是我本人，覺得自己英文不斷在進步，跟外國人說起話來更流利。

本書附有 CD 一片，每個 Unit 有一個 track，每一個 track 重複聽，熟了以後再背更快。

劉 毅

UNIT 1 1~3劇情簡介

【和朋友逛街】

1. ***The weather is gorgeous.***
Everyone wants to go out.
Nobody wants to stay in.

It's a
beautiful day.
（天氣真好。）

We have been shopping
for a while.
My feet are sore.
My patience is running out.

You need a break.
（你需要休息一下。）

You can go walk around.
I'm going to hang out here.
I will wait until you come
back.

See you later.
（待會見。）

*   *   *

【談到自己的太太】

2. ***She didn't respect me.***
She wasn't polite to me.
I'm not at all used to being
treated like that.

Me neither.
（我也不習慣。）

She is very stubborn.
She is narrow-minded.
She never listens to me.

She never listens
to me, either.
(她也從不聽我說話。)

She has a terrible personality.
She isn't satisfied with
    anything.
Nobody likes being
    around her.

I sure don't.
(我當然也不喜歡。)

*   *   *

【談論朋友湯姆遲到】

3. ***Everyone is present except Tom.***
   He hasn't arrived yet.
   He might not be able to catch
       up with us.

That's too bad.
(真糟糕。)

I've been here an hour.
It seems like forever.
I don't feel like waiting any
    longer.

OK, let's go.
(好，走吧。)

I was a little upset.
He arrived very late.
I was made to wait for a long time.

I'm so sorry.
(我為你難過。)

1. The weather is gorgeous.

The weather is *gorgeous*. 【攝南大】	天氣太棒了。
Everyone wants to *go out*.	每個人都想出去玩。
Nobody wants to *stay in*.	沒有人想待在家裡。
We have been shopping *for a while*.	我們已經逛街逛了一段時間。
My feet are *sore*. 【濱松大】	我的腳很痛。
My patience is *running out*.	我快沒有耐心了。
You can *go walk around*.	你可以去四處走走。
I'm going to *hang out here*.	我要待在這裡。
I will wait *until* you come back.	我會等你回來。

【北海學園大】

** —————————————————

gorgeous〔ˈgɔrdʒəs〕*adj.* 非常漂亮的；極好的
go out 出去；出去玩　　*stay in* 待在家裡
sore〔sor〕*adj.* 痛的；酸痛的
patience〔ˈpeʃəns〕*n.* 耐心　　*run out* 耗盡；用完
shop〔ʃap〕*v.* 逛街購物　　*a while* 一段時間
walk around 四處走走　　*hang out* 徘徊；逗留

【背景説明】

　　　　「一口氣英語」是收集美國人説的話編輯而成。既然要背，就要背最好的。如美國人常説：The weather is perfect. 我們改成：The weather is gorgeous. 你説起英文來，就比一般人更好。

1-1　The weather is gorgeous.

> 　　美國人喜歡談論天氣，避免人和人在一起沒話説會尷尬。gorgeous〔'gɔrdʒəs〕*adj.* ①非常漂亮的（= *very beautiful*）②極好的。這句話可加強語氣説成：The weather is **absolutely** gorgeous.（天氣確實很好。）也常説成：The weather is perfect.（天氣太棒了。）或 It's a beautiful day.（天氣太好了。）

absolutely〔'æbsə,lutlɪ〕*adv.* 確實
perfect〔'pɝfɪkt〕*adj.* 完美的；理想的
beautiful〔'bjutəfəl〕*adj.* 漂亮的；很棒的

1-2　Everyone wants to go out.

　　可説成：Everyone wants to go outside.（每個人都想出去。）或 Everyone wants to go outside and enjoy the weather.（每個人都想出去享受美好的天氣。）***go out*** 有很多意思，在這裡是指「出去玩」。

1-3　Nobody wants to stay in.
stay in 待在家裡（= *stay indoors; stay in the house*）

　　可説成：Nobody wants to stay indoors.（沒有人想要待在室內。）【indoors〔ɪn'dorz〕*adv.* 在室內】

1-4　We have been shopping *for a while*.

可加強語氣說成：We have been shopping for quite a while.（我們已經逛街逛了一段很長的時間。）

a while 是「一段時間」，*quite a while* 是「很長的一段時間」（= *a long while* = *a long time*）。

1-5　My feet are sore.

sore〔sor〕*adj.* 痛的；（肌肉）酸痛的，幾乎身體各部位酸痛、疼痛，都可用 sore 或 aching〔'ekɪŋ〕。例如：My neck is sore.（我的脖子痛。）My back is sore.（我的背痛。）My throat is sore.（我的喉嚨痛。）（= *I have a sore throat.*）

這句話也可說成：*I have sore feet*.（我的腳很痛。）或 My feet are killing me.（我的腳痛死了。）或 My feet hurt.（我的腳很痛。）

kill〔kɪl〕*v.*（疼痛部位等）給予（某人）很大的苦痛
hurt〔hɜt〕*v.* 疼痛

1-6　My patience is running out.

run out 耗盡；用完（= *use up*）

可說成：*I'm running out of patience*.（我快沒有耐心了。）或 My patience is almost exhausted.（我快沒有耐心了。）

【run out of 用完　exhaust〔ɪg'zɔst〕*v.* 耗盡】

「現在完成進行式」比「現在完成式」語氣要強，強調正在進行。可改成固定時間，說成：We have been shopping for three hours. (我們已經逛街逛了三個小時。)

1-7 You can go walk *around*.

這句話源自：You can go and walk around. (你可以去四處走走。) 可說成：Go on without me. (不要管我，繼續做你想做的事。) 或 You are free to do your own thing. (你想做什麼就去做什麼。)【***go on*** 繼續】

也可說成：You can go walking around. (你可以去四處走走。) 但不能說：*You can go to walk around.*【文法對，但美國人不用】
現在 go 後面常加原形動詞。【詳見「文法寶典」p.419】

1-8 I'm going to hang out here.

hang 的主要意思是「懸掛」，美國五、六十年代，年輕人喜歡在公園、在牆角坐著不動，像是掛在那裡，所以 hang out here 作「待在這裡」解 (= *hang around here = stay here for a while*)。【詳見「一口氣背會話」p.822】

也可說成：I'm going to hang around here. (我打算待在這裡。) (= *I'm going to stay here.*)

1-9 I will wait *until you come back*.

可說成：I will wait for you to return. (我會等你回來。) 或 I will be waiting for you to return. (我會等你。) 未來進行式有加強語氣的作用。

2. *Nobody likes being around her.*

She didn't respect me.	她不尊敬我。
She wasn't polite to me.	她對我不禮貌。
I'*m not at all used to* being treated like that. 【工學院大】	我非常不習慣被那樣對待。
She is very *stubborn*. 【九州國際大】	她很頑固。
She is *narrow-minded*.	她心胸狹窄。
She never listens to me.	她從不聽我說話。
She has a terrible personality.	她的個性很糟糕。
She *is*n't *satisfied with* anything. 【東北工大】	她對任何事都不滿意。
Nobody *likes being* around her.	沒有人喜歡和她在一起。

** ——————————————

respect〔rɪ'spɛkt〕*v.* 尊敬；尊重
polite〔pə'laɪt〕*adj.* 有禮貌的　　*not at all* 一點也不
be used to + V-ing 習慣於　　treat〔trit〕*v.* 對待
stubborn〔'stʌbən〕*adj.* 頑固的
narrow-minded〔'næro,maɪndɪd〕*adj.* 心胸狹窄的
terrible〔'tɛrəbḷ〕*adj.* 可怕的；糟糕的
personality〔,pɜsṇ'ælətɪ〕*n.* 個性
be satisfied with 對～滿意
around〔ə'raʊnd〕*prep.* 在…周圍

【背景説明】

喜歡抱怨、在背後説別人壞話,中外都是一樣。把心事吐露給自己的好朋友,兩人的關係會更親密。一般美國人你告訴他一個祕密,他通常也會告訴你一個祕密。

2-1 She didn't respect me.

可説成:She wasn't respectful to me. (她不尊敬我。) 或 She showed no respect for me. (她對我不尊敬。)【respectful〔rɪˈspɛktfəl〕adj. 恭敬的】

2-2 She wasn't polite *to me*.

可説成:She was rude to me. (她對我很粗魯。) 或 She was impolite to me. (她對我不禮貌。)
rude〔rud〕adj. 粗魯的;無禮的
impolite〔ˌɪmpəˈlaɪt〕adj. 沒禮貌的

2-3 I*'m not at all **used to** being treated *like that*.
be used to* + *V-ing 習慣於 (= *be accustomed to* + *V-ing*)

可説成:No one ever treats me that way. (沒有人曾經那樣對待我。) 也可簡單説成:I'm not used to being treated like that. (我不習慣被那樣對待。)
【ever〔ˈɛvɚ〕adv. 曾經   that way 那樣】

2-4　She is *very* stubborn.

　　　stubborn〔'stʌbən〕*adj.* 頑固的，從字根上分析，
stub 是「短的」，born 是「出生的」，傳說矮的人比較
「頑固」。可加強語氣說成：She is as stubborn as a
mule. (她像騾子一樣頑固。)【mule〔mjul〕*n.* 騾子】

2-5　She is *narrow-minded*.

　　　narrow-minded 的主要意思是「心胸狹窄的」，相反
詞是 broad-minded「心胸寬大的」(= *open-minded*)。

　　　這句話也可說成：She is close-minded. (她思想僵
化。) 或 She is intolerant of others' opinions. (她不能
容忍別人的意見。)
close-minded〔'klos,maɪndɪd〕*adj.* 思想僵化的；保守的
intolerant〔ɪn'talərənt〕*adj.* 無法容忍的

2-6　She *never* listens to me.

　　　可說成：She doesn't care what I say. (她不在乎
我說什麼。) 或 She never takes my advice. (她從來
不聽我的勸告。)
【care〔kɛr〕*v.* 在乎　take one's advice 聽從某人的勸告】

2-7 She has a terrible personality.

可説成：She's a horrible person. (她很恐怖。) 或
She's just awful. (她真的很糟糕。)

horrible (ˈhɑrəbḷ) *adj.* 可怕的
just (dʒʌst) *adv.* 真地；的確
awful (ˈɔfʊl) *adj.* 可怕的；糟糕的

2-8 She isn't satisfied with anything.

有人就是永遠不滿足，不滿足的人，永遠不會快
樂。所以，可説成：She's never happy. (她永遠不會
快樂。) 或 She's impossible to please. (不可能讓她
高興。)【please (pliz) *v.* 取悅】

2-9 Nobody likes being around her.
= Nobody likes to be around her.

可説成：Everybody avoids her as much as
possible. (每個人都儘可能避開她。) 或 Nobody wants
to hang out with her. (沒有人想要和她在一起。) 狠一
點的説法是：Everybody avoids her like the plague.
(每個人對她都避之唯恐不及。)

avoid (əˈvɔɪd) *v.* 避開   as…as possible 儘可能
hang out with 和～在一起   plague (pleg) *n.* 瘟疫

3. It seems like forever.

Everyone is present except Tom. 【廣島修道大】	除了湯姆，每個人都來了。
He has*n't* arrived *yet*.	他還沒來。
He might not be able to *catch up with* us.	他可能無法趕上我們。
I've been here an hour.	我已經在這裡一個小時了。
It seems *like forever*.	似乎好像很久了。
I don't *feel like* waiting any longer. 【早大】	我不想再等了。
I was a little upset.	我有點生氣。
He arrived very late.	他很晚才到。
I *was made to* wait for a long time. 【千葉工大】	我被迫等很久。

**

except〔ɪk'sɛpt〕*prep.* 除了⋯以外
present〔'prɛznt〕*adj.* 出席的；在場的
not⋯yet 尚未；還沒　　*be able to* + *V.* 能夠~
catch up with 趕上；追上　　seem〔sim〕*v.* 似乎
forever〔fə'ɛvə〕*n.* 很長的一段時間
feel like + *V-ing* 想要~　　*not⋯any longer* 不再⋯
upset〔ʌp'sɛt〕*adj.* 生氣的　　late〔let〕*adv.* 晚地

【背景説明】

　　　「一口氣英語」的每一個句子，都是經
過研究，儘量寫出來源和同義句。越是難的
句子，我們解釋得越清楚，讓你對背的句子
有信心。

3-1　Everyone is present *except Tom*.

　　可説成：Everyone *except Tom* is present.（除了湯
姆以外，每個人都到了。）或 Everyone is here except
Tom.（除了湯姆，每個人都到了。）

3-2　He has*n't* arrived *yet*.
not…yet 尚未

　　可説成：He hasn't come yet.（他還沒來。）或
He's not here yet.（他還沒到。）

3-3　He might not be able to catch up with us.
catch up with 趕上；追上

　　可説成：He might not make it.（他可能無法趕
到。）或 He might not be able to meet us.（他可能
無法和我們會面。）在這裡，用 may 或 might 意思相
同。【make it 成功；辦到；能來】

3-4 I've been here *an hour.*

可説成：I've been here *for an hour.*（我已經在這裡一個小時了。）可加強語氣説成：I've been here for at least an hour.（我已經在這裡至少一個小時了。）或 I've been here for almost an hour.（我已經在這裡快要一個小時了。）【at least　至少】

3-5 It seems *like forever.*

這句話字面的意思是「似乎像是永遠。」引申爲「似乎像是很久了。」(= *It seems like a long time.*)

在這裡，forever 當名詞用，指「很長的一段時間」。也可説成：Time is moving slowly.（時間過得很慢。）或 It feels like a lifetime.（感覺像是過了一輩子。）這都是誇張的用法。

move〔muv〕*v.* 移動；前進
lifetime〔'laɪf,taɪm〕*n.* 一生；終生

3-6 I don't feel like waiting *any longer.*

not…any longer 不再

feel like + V-ing 表示「想要~」。可説成：I'm not waiting any longer.（我不要再等了。）或 I'm not going to wait any longer.（我不想要再等了。）

3-7 I was *a little* upset.

upset〔ʌpˈsɛt〕*adj.* 生氣的

可說成：I was *somewhat* angry.（我有點生氣。）

或 I was *kind of* pissed off.（我有點生氣。）

【pissed off 生氣的（= *angry*）】

somewhat〔ˈsʌmˌhwɑt〕*adv.* 有點
= kind of
= sort of
= a little

3-8 He arrived *very late*.

可簡單說成：He was late.（他來晚了。）或 He was *extremely* late.（他來得非常晚。）

【extremely〔ɪkˈstrimlɪ〕*adv.* 非常】

3-9 I was made to wait *for a long time*.
　　　　　　主　詞　補　語

主動的說法是：He made *me* wait for a long time.
　　　　　　　　　　受詞　　　受詞補語

當受詞變成主詞，受詞補語就變成主詞補語，此時不定詞片語要有 to。【詳見「文法寶典」p.381】

UNIT1 4~6劇情簡介

【和朋友談到一本書】

4. ***I know all about that book.***
I read it before.
You should put it on your
reading list.

Thanks for the tip.
（謝謝你的建議。）

This novel is worth reading
from cover to cover.
It's a fascinating story.
It's one of my favorites.

Thanks for the
recommendation.
（謝謝你的推薦。）

I was so absorbed in the
book.
It was a real page-turner.
I kept reading through
lunch and dinner.

I noticed that.
（我有注意到。）

* * *

【向別人介紹自己的朋友】

5. ***We are buddies.***
We have done a lot together.
We've known each other for
ages.

Wow!
（哇！）

He is very well-paid.
His business is booming.
He is rich enough to buy
  anything.

Must be nice.
(一定很棒。)

He can barely speak English.
He had no clear-cut plan.
He was foolish to go overseas.

He made a poor
  decision.
(他做了很糟的決定。)

*　*　*

【迷路的時候說】

6. *I have been walking for an hour.*
   I haven't gotten there yet.
   Are these the right directions to
     get there?

Yes.
(是的。)

I may have lost my way.
I think I need some assistance.
Is there anyone to help me out?

Ask
  somebody.
(問別人。)

I didn't prepare well.
I didn't give it my all.
I'm deeply disappointed with
  myself.

Everybody
  fails at
  some time.
(每個人在某個時
  候都會失誤。)

4. *It was a real page-turner*.

I *know all about* that book. 【阪南大】	我非常了解那本書。
I read it before.	我以前讀過。
You should put it on your *reading list*.	你應該把它放在你的閱讀書單 上。
This novel *is worth reading* from cover to cover.【中京大】	這本小說值得從頭讀到尾。
It's a *fascinating* story.	這是一個很有趣的故事。
It's one of my *favorites*.	它是我最喜愛的小說之一。
I *was* so *absorbed in* the book.【廣島女學院大】	我迷上這本書。
It was a real *page-turner*.	這本書一看就停不下來。
I kept reading *through* *lunch and dinner*.	我一直讀，連午餐和晚餐都在讀。

** ────────────────

reading list 閱讀書單　　novel〔ˈnɑvḷ〕*n.* 小說
be worth + V-ing 值得～　　cover〔ˈkʌvɚ〕*n.* 封面
from cover to cover （整本書）從頭到尾
fascinating〔ˈfæsn̩͵etɪŋ〕*adj.* 迷人的；吸引人的；有趣的
favorite〔ˈfevərɪt〕*n.* 最喜愛的人或物
be absorbed in 專心於；沈迷於
page-turner〔ˈpedʒ͵tʒnɚ〕*n.* 令人欲罷不能的書
through〔θru〕*prep.* 在整個…期間

【背景説明】

學英文最快的方法，就是先學會説，就像小
孩子，從小跟著媽媽説，會説話之後才上學。英
文不會説，學起來會更辛苦。會説英文以後，有
了感覺，再做考題練習，進步神速。

4-1 I know all about that book.

這句話字面的意思是「我知道所有關於那本書的事。」
引申爲「我很熟悉那本書。」（= *I'm familiar with that book.*）或 I'm well acquainted with that book.（我非常了解那本書。）【be acquainted with 認識；了解】

4-2 I read it *before*.

before 單獨使用時，可以和「現在完成式」或「過去簡單式」連用。這句話也可説成：I've read it before.（我以前讀過。）【詳見「文法寶典」p.247】

4-3 You should put it *on your reading list*.

這句話字面的意思是「你應該把這本書放在你的閱讀書單上。」引申爲「你應該看這本書。」（= *It belongs on your reading list.*）可簡單説成：You should read it.（你應該看這本書。）

美國人很喜歡用 list，如去買東西，手上會拿著 shopping list（購物清單），每天要做什麼事，會先寫一張 to-do list（待辦事項），出國旅行的時候，會列出一張 packing list（裝箱單）。【pack〔pæk〕v. 打包】

4-4　This novel is worth reading *from cover to cover.*

worth 後面加動名詞，必須是主動的及物動詞，但無受詞。如用 worthy，就要用被動，說成：This novel is worthy of being read from cover to cover.（這本小說值得從頭讀到尾。）

cover 是「封面」，*from cover to cover*「從封面到封底」，引申為「從頭到尾；從第一頁到最後一頁」，也可說成：*from front to back*（從正面到背面），或 *from start to finish*（從開始到結束）（= *from beginning to end*）。

4-5　It's a *fascinating* story.

fascinating 的主要意思是「迷人的；吸引人的」，還可作「有趣的」解。如你看到一個好地方，你可以說：This is a *fascinating* place.（這是一個迷人的地方。）看到一個美女，你可以說：She is a *fascinating* person.（她很有吸引力。）

這句話也可說成：It's an excellent story.（這是一個很棒的故事。）（= *It's a wonderful story.*）

【excellent〔ˈɛksḷənt〕*adj.* 極好的】

4-6　It's one *of my favorites.*

favorite 主要是當形容詞用，作「最喜愛的」解，當名詞時，是指「最喜愛的人或物」。可說成：It's a favorite of mine.（這是我最喜愛的書。）

4-7 I *was so absorbed in* the book.

　　也可說成：I was engrossed in the book.（我迷上這本書。）(= *I was lost in the book.*)

> *be absorbed in*　專心於；沈迷於
> = *be engrossed in*
> = *be lost in*

4-8 It was a *real* page-turner.

　　page-turner 字面的意思是「翻頁的東西」，好看的書會使人不停地翻頁，引申為「令人欲罷不能的書；扣人心弦的讀物」(= *a book that is very exciting*)。這句話也可說成：It kept my interest from page to page.（每一頁都使我覺得有趣。）

4-9 I kept reading *through lunch and dinner.*

　　字面的意思是「我午餐和晚餐都一直在讀。」就像中文的「我廢寢忘食地看書。」也可說成：I forgot to eat.（我忘記吃東西。）或 I skipped lunch and dinner in order to keep reading the book.（為了持續看這本書，我午餐和晚餐都沒吃。）【skip〔skɪp〕v. 省去（某餐）不吃】或說成：I kept reading during lunch and dinner.（我吃午餐和晚餐時都一直在看。）

　　read 是及物和不及物兩用動詞，在這裡美國人較不習慣說：*I kept reading it through lunch and dinner.* 但可說：I kept reading the book through lunch and dinner.

5. *His business is booming*.

We are buddies. 【七試】	我們是朋友。
We have done a lot together.	我們一起做過很多事。
We've known each other *for ages*.	我們彼此認識很久了。
He is very *well-paid*. 【國學院大】	他賺了很多錢。
His business is *booming*.	他的事業興隆。
He is rich enough to buy anything.	他很有錢，能買任何東西。
He can barely speak English.	他不太會說英文。
He had no *clear-cut* plan.	他沒有明確的計劃。
He was foolish to *go overseas*.	他出國真是愚蠢。

【四天王寺國際敎大】

** ───────────

buddy〔'bʌdɪ〕*n.* 朋友
ages〔'edʒɪz〕*n. pl.* 長時間　*for ages* 很久
well-paid〔'wɛl'ped〕*adj.* 高薪的；報酬豐厚的
boom〔bum〕*v.* 繁榮；快速成長
barely〔'bɛrlɪ〕*adv.* 幾乎不（= *hardly*）
clear-cut〔'klɪr,kʌt〕*adj.* 明確的
foolish〔'fulɪʃ〕*adj.* 愚蠢的
overseas〔'ovɚ'siz〕*adv.* 到國外
go overseas 出國（= *go abroad*）

【背景説明】

　　　　每天背「一口氣英語」，不會無聊。睡前背
一背，很快會睡著。背完之後，找機會使用，説
出新的句子，你會感覺到越來越進步。

5-1　We are buddies.

buddy〔ˈbʌdɪ〕*n.* 朋友

　　可説成：We are pals. (我們是好朋友。) (= *We are good friends.*) pal〔pæl〕*n.* 朋友；好友，pen pal 是「筆友」。

5-2　We have done a lot *together*.

　　可説成：We have been through a lot together.
(我們一起經歷過很多事。) 或 We have shared many experiences. (我們有很多共同的經驗。)

【through〔θru〕*prep.* 經歷　　share〔ʃɛr〕*v.* 分享；共有】

5-3　We've known each other *for ages*.

ages〔ˈedʒɪz〕*n. pl.* 很長的時間

for ages 很久 (= *for a long time*)

　　可説成：We've known each other for a long time. (我們認識很久了。) 或 We've known each other for years. (我們認識好多年了。)

years〔jɪrz〕*n. pl.* 很久 (= *a very long time*)

for years 好多年

5-4 He is *very well-paid*.

這句話有兩個意思：①他的薪水很高。(= *His salary is very high*.) ②他賺很多錢。(= *He makes a lot of money*.) 可指老板或員工。

5-5 His business is *booming*.

boom 這個字的主要意思是「發出隆隆聲」，在這裡作「繁榮；迅速發展」解。Business is booming! 是指「生意興隆！」

這句話的意思是「他的事業興隆。」也可說成：His business is growing. (他的事業越做越大。) (= *His business is doing well*.)

booming 這個字常在報紙上出現，如 The smart phone market is *booming*. (智慧型手機市場越來越興盛。) 或 Taipei has a *booming* economy. (台北的經濟很繁榮。)

【grow〔gro〕*v*. 成長　do〔du〕*v*. 進展】

5-6 He is rich *enough to buy anything*.

可說成：He can buy whatever he wants. (他可以買任何他想要的東西。) 或 There's nothing he can't buy. (沒有什麼東西是他不能買的。)

5-7　He can *barely* speak English.

barely〔'bɛrlɪ〕*adv.* 幾乎不 (= *hardly*)

可說成：His English is poor. (他的英文很差。) 或

His English is awful. (他的英文很糟糕。)

【poor〔pʊr〕*adj.* 差勁的　　awful〔'ɔfʊl〕*adj.* 糟糕的】

5-8　He had no clear-cut plan.

可說成：He had no idea what he was doing. (他

不知道自己在做什麼。) 或 He was aimless. (他沒有目

標。)

【*have no idea* 不知道　　aimless〔'emlɪs〕*adj.* 無目標的】

5-9　He was foolish *to go overseas*.

可說成：It was foolish of him to go overseas.

(他出國真是愚蠢。) (= *He was foolish to go abroad.*)

或 He made a big mistake by going abroad. (他出國

是一大錯誤。)

make a mistake 犯錯

abroad〔ə'brɔd〕*adv.* 到國外　　go abroad 出國

6. *I'm deeply disappointed with myself.*

I have been walking for an hour. 【獨協大】	我已經走了一個小時。
I have*n't* gotten there *yet*.	我還沒到那裡。
Are these *the right directions* to get there?	到那裡的方向是正確的嗎？
I may have lost my way. 【京都産業大】	我可能已經迷路了。
I think I need some *assistance*.	我想我需要一些協助。
Is there anyone to *help me out*?	有人可以幫助我嗎？
I didn't prepare well. 【昭和女子大】	我沒有準備好。
I didn't *give it my all*.	我沒有盡全力。
I*'m* deeply *disappointed with* myself.	我對自己很失望。

** ────────────────

not···yet 尚未···　　direction〔dəˈrɛkʃən〕*n.* 方向
lose one's way 迷路（= *be lost*）
assistance〔əˈsɪstəns〕*n.* 協助　　*help sb. out* 幫助某人
prepare〔prɪˈpɛr〕*v.* 準備　　*give it one's all* 盡全力
deeply〔ˈdiplɪ〕*adv.* 深深地
disappointed〔ˌdɪsəˈpɔɪntɪd〕*adj.* 失望的
be disappointed with 對～失望

【背景説明】

中文很少説「我對自己很失望」，可是美國人卻常説：I'm deeply disappointed with myself. 這是中外文化不同。美國人做錯了，都會自己檢討。唯有背美國人所説的話，説起來才像他們。

6-1 I have been walking *for an hour*.

可説成：I've been on foot for an hour.（我已經走了一個小時。）或 An hour has passed since I started walking.（從我開始走路以來，已經過了一個小時。）

【on foot 徒步　　pass〔pæs〕v. 過去】

6-2 I haven't gotten there yet.

可説成：I'm still not there.（我還沒到。）（= *I'm not there yet.*）

6-3 Are these the *right* directions *to get there*?

可説成：Am I going the right way?（我路是不是走對了？）或 Is this the right way to get there?（到那裡，這條路對不對？）

去某地的「方向」不只一個，不是一直向前走，有轉彎等，所以用複數形。

6-4　I may have lost my way.

　　lose one's *way*　迷路（ = *be lost*）

　　　　美國人也常説：I think I'm lost.（我想我迷路了。）
或 Perhaps I've lost my way.（也許我迷路了。）

6-5　I think I need some assistance.

　　　　可説成：I need some help.（我需要一些幫助。）或
I probably need some assistance.（我可能需要一些協
助。）

6-6　Is there anyone *to help me out*?

　　　　可簡單説成：Is there anyone to help me?（有沒有
人可以幫助我？）help me out 和 help me 意思相同，都
是「幫助我」，但 help me out 通常指較小的事。

　　　　這句話也可説成：Can anyone help me?（有沒有人
能幫助我？）或 Can anyone assist me?（有沒有人能協助
我？）【assist〔ə'sɪst〕*v.* 協助】

6-7　I didn't prepare *well*.

　　　　可説成：I wasn't ready for this.（我沒準備好。）
或 I didn't make the necessary preparations.（我沒有
做好必要的準備。）
　　【preparation〔͵prɛpə'reʃən〕*n.* 準備】

6-8 I didn't give it my all.

　　美國人也常説：I didn't give my best effort.（我沒有盡全力。）或 I should have tried harder.（我當時應該更努力才對。）

give one's best effort　盡力（＝ *try one's best*）

should have + p.p.　早該【過去該做而未做】

try hard　努力（＝ *work hard*）

6-9 I'm *deeply* disappointed with myself.

　　美國人也常説成：I've really let myself down.（我眞的讓自己很失望。）或 I failed myself.（我使自己失望。）

【let sb. down　使某人失望　　fail〔fel〕*v.* 失敗；使失望】

　　這句話常常用來檢討自己，激勵自己進步。如：

A: Are you satisfied with your test results?

　　（你對你的考試成績滿意嗎？）

B: I'm deeply disappointed with myself.

　　（我對自己非常失望。）

UNIT 1 7~9劇情簡介

【向別人借筆，寄包裹給暗戀的對象】

7. ***May I borrow a pen?***
    Can you lend me something
        to write with?
    Even a pencil will do.

Here you go.
(拿去吧。)

I sent it out today.
I registered the package.
By next week, she will have
    received it.

Indeed, she will.
(她一定會收到。)

Once I had a secret crush.
She was a classmate from
    long ago.
I have no idea if I will see
    her again.

You never know.
(誰知道。)

*   *   *

I always
eat at home.
(我總是在家吃。)

【習慣早起、喜歡英文、想去美國】

8. ***I'm up at dawn every day.***
    I dress fast and leave.
    On my way to work, I usually
        buy breakfast.

I'm crazy about English.
I practice every chance I get.
Traveling to the States
is my dream.

I hope it
comes true
(我希望你的夢
會實現。

I've seen Europe.
It didn't impress me.
It wasn't a big deal.

I thought it was
amazing.
(我以為歐洲很棒

* * *

【和朋友講電話】

9. *I can't talk right now.*
I'm busy at the moment.
Can I call you back later?

Whenever is
good for yc
(你方便的時候
可以。)

Come see me anytime.
You're always welcome.
Are you doing anything
tomorrow?

Nope, no plans.
(沒有,沒有計畫

I don't know if he will
show up.
He hasn't answered my call.
Let's go without him.

Let's go
(走吧。)

7. *She was a classmate from long ago*.

May I borrow a pen?	我可以借一枝筆嗎？
Can you *lend* me something to write with? 【神戶松蔭女子學院大】	你可以借我一個東西來寫字嗎？
Even a pencil will *do*.	就算是鉛筆也可以。
I sent it out today. 【七試】	我今天把它寄出去了。
I *registered* the package.	我用掛號寄那個包裹。
By next week, she will have received it.	到了下禮拜，她就會收到。
Once I had a secret crush. 【玉川大】	從前我有個暗戀的對象。
She was a classmate *from long ago*.	她是我很久以前的同學。
I have no idea *if* I will see her again.	我不知道我是否會再見到她。

** ———————————

borrow〔'baro〕v. 借（入）　　lend〔lɛnd〕v. 借（出）
do〔du〕v. 行；可以　　register〔'rɛdʒɪstɚ〕v. 以掛號郵寄
package〔'pækɪdʒ〕n. 包裹　　by〔baɪ〕prep. 到了；在～之前
once〔wʌns〕adv. 曾經；從前
secret〔'sikrɪt〕adj. 祕密的　　crush〔krʌʃ〕n. 迷戀的對象
a secret crush 暗戀的對象　　*long ago* 很久以前
I have no idea 我不知道（= *I don't know*）

【背景說明】

學英文文法是學語言的捷徑，學不完全，就變成絆腳石，會因為有限的文法規則而不敢造句。如 by next week，往往和「未來完成式」連用，但「假設法」沒有「未來完成式」，該怎麼辦？這一回就有說明。

7-1 May I borrow a pen?

可說成：Can I borrow a pen?（我能借一枝筆嗎？）或 Do you have a pen I can borrow?（你有沒有筆我可以借？）

7-2 Can you <u>lend</u> <u>me</u> <u>something</u> *to write with*?
　　　　　 授與動詞 間受　直　受

borrow 和 lend 都是「借」，borrow 直接接受詞，但是 lend 要接間接受詞和直接受詞。

【比較】 Can I <u>borrow</u> <u>something</u> to write with?
　　　　　 及物動詞　　受　詞
（我可以借個東西來寫字嗎？）

Can I 和 May I 意思相同，但 May 較有禮貌。

7-3 *Even a* pencil will do.

even 和 only 都是可修飾名詞的副詞。這句話可簡單說成：A pencil will do.（一枝鉛筆就行了。）do 在此是「完全不及物動詞」，作「行；可以」解（= *be good enough*）。常見的有：*That will do*.（行，行，行。）*That won't do*.（不行。）

7-4 I sent it *out today*.

　　send 的主要意思是「送」，在此作「寄」解。
send sth. out 是「寄出某物」。這句話可簡單說成：I sent
it today.（我今天把它寄出去了。）或 I mailed it today.
（我今天把它寄出去了。）【mail〔mel〕*v.* 郵寄】

7-5 I registered the package.

　　register 的主要的意思是「登記；註冊」，在此作
「以掛號寄出」解。可說成：I sent the package via
registered mail.（我用掛號寄出那個包裹。）或 The
package is registered.（包裹是掛號寄出的。）
【via〔'vaɪə〕*prep.* 經由；以；藉　　registered mail　掛號郵件】

7-6 *By next week*, she will have received it.
= Next week, she will receive it.

　　by next week「到下禮拜」，和「未來完成式」運用，
表未來將完成的動作。可說成：She should get it *by next
week*.（她應該下禮拜就會收到。）should 是假設法助動詞，
假設法沒有「未來完成式」，所以用「should + 原形 V.」
代替。這句話也可說成：It should be there sometime
next week.（下個禮拜某時應該就會到。）
【sometime〔'sʌm‚taɪm〕*adv.* 某時】

7-7 *Once* I had a secret crush.

　　crush 的主要意思是「壓碎」，在此作「迷戀的對象」
解。*a secret crush* 是指「暗戀的對象」。

可說成：I once had *a secret crush*. (從前我有一個
暗戀的對象。) 或 I used to have *a secret crush*. (我以
前有一個暗戀的對象。) 【used to V. 以前~】

7-8　She was a classmate *from long ago*.
　　　　　　　　　　= from a long time ago

　　　很多人搞不清楚，爲什麼用 *from long ago*？在字
典上，作「從很久以前開始」解，在這裡是形容詞片語，
修飾 classmate。不可說成：*of long ago* (誤)。
from 後面還可接其他名詞，如：

　　She was a classmate *from college*.
　　(她是我的大學同學。)

　　She was a classmate *from junior high*.
　　(她是我的國中同學。)
　　【*junior high* 國中 (=*junior high school*)】

from long ago 也可說成 from a long time ago。

7-9　I have no idea *if I will see her again*.
　　　　　　whether　名 詞 子 句

　　　I have no idea「我不知道」(=*I don't know*)，後面
的 if 引導名詞子句，if 作「是否」解 (=*whether*)，否則
就不能用 will 表示未來了。也可說成：I'll probably
never see her again. (我也許永遠不會再見到她。) 或
Who knows if I'll ever see her again. (誰知道我是否
會再見到她。) 【ever = at any time】

8. I'm up at dawn every day.

I'm up at dawn every day.	我每天天亮就起床。
I dress *fast* and leave.	我很快把衣服穿好，然後出門。
On my way to work, I usually buy breakfast. 【明治大】	在上班途中，我通常會買早餐。
I'm crazy about English.	我熱愛英文。
I practice *every chance I get*. 【松山大】	我一有機會就練習。
Traveling to the States is *my dream*.	去美國旅行是我的夢想。
I've seen Europe. 【阪南大】	我去過歐洲觀光。
It didn't *impress me*.	我覺得不怎麼樣。
It wasn't *a big deal*.	沒什麼大不了。

** ───────────────

be up 起床（= *get up*）
dawn〔dɔn〕*n.* 黎明；天亮　　dress〔drɛs〕*v.* 穿衣服
on one's way to work 在某人上班途中
be crazy about 熱愛　　practice〔'præktɪs〕*v.* 練習
the States 美國　　see〔si〕*v.* 參觀；遊覽
impress〔ɪm'prɛs〕*v.* 使印象深刻
a big deal 了不起的事

【背景説明】

有一些句子，文法上沒辦法解釋，這樣的句子最精彩，例如：I practice every chance I get. 非背不行，因爲 chance 不是 practice 的受詞。

8-1 I'm up *at dawn every day.*

be up 起床（= *get up* = *wake up*）

dawn〔dɔn〕*n.* 黎明；天亮，at dawn 是「天亮時」（= *at sunrise* = *at daybreak* = *at first light*）。

可説成：I get up at dawn every day.（我每天天亮就起床。）（= *I wake up at dawn every day.*）或 I get up early every day.（我每天都很早就起床。）可加強語氣，幽默説成：I'm up at the crack of dawn every single day.（我每天天一亮就起床。）

crack〔kræk〕*n.* 裂縫　　at the crack of dawn 黎明時
single〔ˈsɪŋgl̩〕*adj.* 單一的

8-2 I dress *fast* and leave.

dress 是「穿衣服」，也可説成 get dressed。美國人也常説：I get dressed and leave quickly.（我很快把衣服穿好，然後出門。）或 I put on my clothes and leave.（我穿上衣服，然後就出門。）句中 put on my clothes「穿上我的衣服」也可説成 put my clothes on。

8-3　On my way *to work*, I *usually* buy breakfast.

　　「上班途中」是 ***on my way to work***，「上學途中」
是 ***on my way to school***，「回家途中」是 ***on my way
home***。

　　這句話也可說成：I usually buy breakfast on my
way to work. (我通常在上班途中買早餐。) 或 Generally
speaking, I buy breakfast on my way to work. (一般
說來，我都在上班途中買早餐。) 注意，三餐名詞前不加冠
詞。【generally speaking 一般說來】

8-4　I'm crazy about English.

be crazy about　熱愛 (= *be mad about*)

　　可說成：I'm mad about English. (我熱愛英文。)
或 I love English very much. (我很愛英文。)

8-5　I practice *every chance I get*.

　　這句話是慣用語，源自：I practice ***every time*** *I get
a chance*. (一有機會我就練習。) 還可說成：I never
miss a chance to practice. (我從來不會錯過練習的機會。)
【miss〔mɪs〕*v.* 錯過】

8-6　<u>Traveling *to the States*</u> is my dream.
　　　　　主　　詞

　　　動名詞片語當主詞，用單數動詞 is。也可說成：My dream is to travel to the States. (我的夢想是到美國旅遊。) 或 Traveling to the U.S. is my goal. (到美國旅遊是我的目標。)【goal〔gol〕*n.* 目標】

8-7　I've seen Europe.

　　　　see 在此作「參觀；遊覽」解。例如：I've always wanted to see America. (我一直想去美國觀光。)

　　　這句話也可說成：I've been to Europe. (我去過歐洲。) 或 I've visited Europe. (我去過歐洲觀光。)

　　【have been to　曾經去過】

8-8　It didn't impress me.

　　　這句話字面的意思是「它使我印象不深刻。」引申為「我覺得它不怎麼樣。」(= *I wasn't impressed.* = *It wasn't impressive.*)　　impressed〔ɪm'prɛst〕*adj.* (人) 印象深刻的 impressive〔ɪm'prɛsɪv〕*adj.* 令人印象深刻的

8-9　It wasn't a big deal.
　　　a big deal 了不起的事

　　　可說成：It was nothing special. (它沒什麼特別的。)(= *It wasn't anything special.*)

9. *Are you doing anything tomorrow?*

I can't talk right now. 【松山大】	我現在不能說話。
I'm busy *at the moment*.	我目前很忙。
Can I *call* you *back* later?	我可以待會再回你電話嗎？
Come see me anytime. 【中京大】	隨時來看我。
You're always *welcome*.	我永遠都歡迎你。
Are you doing anything tomorrow? 【中京大】	你明天有空嗎？
I don't know *if* he will show up. 【流通經濟大】	我不知道他是否會出現。
He hasn't *answered my call*.	他沒接我的電話。
Let's go *without him*.	我們走吧，不管他。

** ─────────────

right now 現在　　*at the moment* 此刻；目前
call sb. back 回某人電話　　later〔'letɚ〕*adv.* 待會
anytime〔'ɛnɪˌtaɪm〕*adv.* 在任何時候
show up 出現 (= *turn up* = *appear*)
answer one's call 接某人的電話

【背景說明】

說英文要慢慢說，越慢越好。如果模糊帶過，雖然外國人聽得懂，但你會進步得很慢。即使是你背過的句子，也要慢慢說。

9-1 I can't talk *right now*.

可說成：***Right now*** is not a good time to talk.
（現在不方便和你說話。）或 I can't speak with you
right now.（我現在沒辦法和你說話。）

9-2 I'm busy *at the moment*.

at the moment 的意思是「此刻；目前」(= *now*
= *right now*)。可簡單說成：I'm busy.（我很忙。）或
I'm busy right now.（我現在很忙。）

9-3 Can I call you *back later*?

可加強語氣說成：Would it be OK if I return your
call at a later time?（如果我晚一點回你電話可以嗎？）
return one's call 回某人電話
later〔'letɚ〕*adj.* 較晚的

9-4　*Come see me anytime.*

可加長為：Come see me whenever you feel like it. (無論何時你想來，就來看我。) (= *Come see me whenever you want.*)【come + 原形 V. 的用法，詳見「文法寶典」p.419】

9-5　You're *always* welcome.

可說成：My door is always open. (隨時歡迎你。) 或 My home is your home. (我家就是你家。) 也可加長為：You're always welcome to stay here. (永遠歡迎你住在這裡。)【stay〔ste〕*v.* 暫住】

9-6　Are you doing anything *tomorrow*?

這句話字面的意思是「明天你有要做什麼事嗎？」引申為「你明天有空嗎？」(= *Are you free tomorrow?*) 也可說成：Are you busy tomorrow? (你明天忙嗎？) 或 Do you have any plans for tomorrow? (你明天有任何計劃嗎？) 會說 Are you doing anything tomorrow? 外國人會感覺到你的英文很棒。

9-7 I don't know *if he will show up*.

名 詞 子 句

show up 出現 (= *turn up* = *appear*)

可説成：I'm not sure if he will turn up.（我不確定他是否會出現。）或 It's not certain that he will show up.（不確定他是否會出現。）

9-8 He hasn't answered my call.

可説成：He didn't answer my call.（他沒有接我的電話。）(= *He is not taking my call.*) 或 He's not picking up the phone.（他沒接電話。）或簡單説成：He's not picking up.（他沒接電話。）

「應門」是 answer the door，「接電話」是 answer the call 或 pick up the phone。

9-9 Let's go *without him*.

可説成：Let's not wait for him.（我們不要等他。）或 Let's just leave without him.（我們走就對了，不管他。）

一口氣考試英語 Unit 1

※ 以三組爲一個單位較好背。

1. **The weather is gorgeous**. 【攝南大】
   Everyone wants to **go out**.
   Nobody wants to **stay in**.

   We have been shopping **for a while**.
   My feet are **sore**. 【濱松大】
   My patience is **running out**.

   You can **go walk around**.
   I'm going to **hang out here**.
   I will wait **until** you come back.
   【北海學園大】

2. She didn't respect me.
   She wasn't polite to me.
   I**'m** not at all **used to** being treated like that. 【工學院大】

   She is very **stubborn**. 【九州國際大】
   She is **narrow-minded**.
   She never listens to me.

   She has a terrible personality.
   She isn't **satisfied with** anything.
   【東北工大】
   Nobody **likes being** around her.

3. Everyone is present except Tom.
   【廣島修道大】
   He has**n't** arrived **yet**.
   He might not be able to **catch up with** us.

I've been here an hour.
It seems **like forever**.
I don't **feel like** waiting any longer. 【早大】

I was a little upset.
He arrived very late.
I **was made to** wait for a long time. 【千葉工大】

* * *

4. **I know all about that book**.
   【阪南大】
   I read it before.
   You should put it on your **reading list**.

   This novel is worth reading from cover to cover. 【中京大】
   It's a **fascinating** story.
   It's one of my **favorites**.

   I **was** so **absorbed in** the book. 【廣島女學院大】
   It was a real **page-turner**.
   I kept reading **through lunch and dinner**.

5. We are buddies. 【ヤ試】
   We have done a lot together.
   We've known each other **for ages**.

He is very *well-paid*. 【國學院大】
His business is *booming*.
He is rich enough to buy
  anything.

He can barely speak English.
He had no *clear-cut* plan.
He was foolish to *go overseas*.
  【四天王寺國際教大】

6. I have been walking for an
   hour. 【獨協大】
   I have*n't* gotten there *yet*.
   Are these *the right directions*
     to get there?

   I may have lost my way.
     【京都産業大】
   I think I need some *assistance*.
   Is there anyone to *help me out*?

   I didn't prepare well. 【昭和女子大】
   I didn't *give it my all*.
   I*'m* deeply *disappointed with*
     myself.

         *   *   *

7. *May I borrow a pen?*
   Can you *lend* me something to
     write with? 【神戶松蔭女子學院大】
   Even a pencil will *do*.

   I sent it out today. 【ヤ試】
   I *registered* the package.
   By next week, she will have
     received it.

※ 可將這兩頁用手機拍下來背。

Once I had a secret crush.
  【玉川大】
She was a classmate *from
  long ago*.
I have no idea *if* I will see
  her again.

8. I'm up at dawn every day.
   I dress *fast* and leave.
   On my way to work, I usually
     buy breakfast. 【明治大】

   I'm crazy about English.
   I practice *every chance I get*.
     【松山大】
   Traveling to the States is *my
     dream*.

   I've seen Europe. 【阪南大】
   It didn't *impress me*.
   It wasn't *a big deal*.

9. I can't talk right now. 【松山大】
   I'm busy *at the moment*.
   Can I *call* you *back* later?

   Come see me anytime. 【中京大】
   You're always *welcome*.
   Are you doing anything
     tomorrow? 【中京大】

   I don't know *if* he will show
     up. 【流通経済大】
   He hasn't *answered my call*.
   Let's go *without him*.

UNIT 2　1~3劇情簡介

【周末休閒看電影】

1. ***Our work is done.***
   Now, we can relax.
   It's such a lovely day that
   　　everybody feels like going

Me too.
（我也是。）

I don't read much.
Watching movies is like a
　　kind of reading to me.
Reading is to the mind what
　　exercise is to the body.

I enjoy reading.
（我愛閱讀。）

It being Sunday, the theater
　　will be crowded.
It won't be easy getting tickets.
Why don't we go on a weekday?

That's a
good idea.
（好主意。）

*　*　*

【給遲到找理由】

2. ***I'm sorry I made you wait.***
   It couldn't be helped.
   A traffic jam prevented me
   　　from arriving on time.

No problem.
（沒問題。）

I didn't sleep well.
I tossed and turned all night.
The bed I slept in wasn't
very comfortable.

Sounds awful.
(聽起來很糟。)

I'm a responsible person.
I'm always on time.
As far as work is concerned,
I always try to do my best.

You're a good
employee.
(你是好員工。)

* * *

【勸人減肥，要先說好聽的話】

3. *I'll be with you.*
I'll support you.
As long as I live, I will not let
you go hungry.

Thanks.
(謝謝。)

Are you still eating?
It's not good for you.
You cannot lose weight until
you give up eating between
meals.

Oh, that's
good advice.
(哦，你的建議很好)

Old habits die hard.
Old dogs cannot learn new tricks.
A bad habit, once formed, cannot
easily be gotten rid of.

This is tru
(真是這樣)

1. It won't be easy getting tickets.

Our work *is done*.	我們的工作做完了。
Now, we can *relax*.	現在，我們可以放輕鬆了。
It's such a lovely day that everybody *feels like going* out.【東京經濟大】	天氣這麼好，每個人都想出去玩。
I don't *read much*.	我很少讀書。
Watching movies is like a kind of reading to me.	看電影對我來說就像是一種閱讀。
Reading is to the mind *what* exercise is to the body.【駒澤大】	閱讀之於心靈，猶如運動之於身體。
It being Sunday, the theater will be crowded.【北海學園大】	因為是禮拜天，所以電影院人會很多。
It won't be easy *getting tickets*.	不容易買到票。
Why don't we go *on a weekday*?	我們何不平日去？

** ——————————

relax〔rɪˈlæks〕*v.* 放鬆
lovely〔ˈlʌvlɪ〕*adj.* 可愛的；極好的
feel like + V-ing 想要～　　much〔mʌtʃ〕*adv.* 常常
A is to B what C is to D. A 之於 B，猶如 C 之於 D。
crowded〔ˈkraʊdɪd〕*adj.* 擁擠的
weekday〔ˈwikˌde〕*n.* 平日

【背景説明】

    有些句子如果不背，很難造出來，像：It being Sunday, the theater will be crowded. 句中的 It being Sunday 有誰能夠造出來？背實用的句子是學英文最簡單的方法。

1-1 Our work *is done*.

  這句話也可說成：Our work is finished. (我們的工作做完了。) 或 Our work is complete. (我們的工作完成了。) Our work 也換成 Our job，説成：Our job is done. (工作已經做完了。)（ = *The work is done.*)

1-2 *Now*, we can *relax*.

  這句話的意思是「現在，我們可以放輕鬆了。」（ = *Now, we can take it easy.*) 也可説成：Now, we can take a break. (現在我們可以休息一下。)
【take it easy 放輕鬆 take a break 休息一下】

1-3 It's *such a lovely* day *that* *everybody feels like going out*.

  也可説成：It's such a nice day that everybody wants to be outdoors. (這麼好的天氣，每個人都想待在戶外。) 或 It's so nice out that nobody wants to be indoors. (外面天氣這麼好，沒有人想要待在室內。)

1-4 I don't read *much*.

  也可説成：I seldom read. (我很少讀書。) 或 I hardly ever read. (我很少讀書。)【hardly ever 很少】

1-5　Watching movies is like a kind of reading *to me*.
　　　　　S.　　　　　　　V.

也可説成：Movies are very similar to books,
I think. (我認為電影很像書本。) 或 Watching a film
is like reading to me. (看電影對我來說就像閱讀。)

【比較】　Watching movies【正】
　　　　　Watching a movie【正】
　　　　　Seeing a movie【正】　　　} is like....
　　　　　Seeing movies【誤】
　　　　　Seeing movies 為什麼不行？找不出理由，
　　　　　所以要背句子最保險。

1-6　Reading is to the mind *what* exercise is to the body.

A is to B { *what* / *as* } *C is to D*.　A 之於 B，猶如 C 之於 D。

這句話也可説成：Reading is to the mind as
exercise is to the body. (閱讀之於心靈，猶如運動之於身
體。)(= *As exercise is to the body, so reading is to the
mind.*)【詳見「文法寶典」p.157, 502】

1-7　*It being Sunday*, the theater will be crowded.

這句話源自：As it is Sunday, the theater will
be crowded. (因為是禮拜天，電影院人會很多。)【As 在此
等於 Because (因為)】可簡化為：The theater is always
crowded on Sunday. (電影院禮拜天總是人很多。)也
可説成：It being Sunday, there will be many people

in the theater. (因為是禮拜天，電影院會有很多人。) 中文説「人很多」，美國人較喜歡用 crowded (擁擠的) 來形容。句中動詞 will be，可用現在式 is 代替。

1-8 It won't be easy *getting tickets*.
　　　 虛主詞　　　　　　　　　　　 眞　主　詞

　　　可用不定詞當眞主詞，説成：It won't be easy to get tickets. (不容易買到票。) 也可説成：Getting tickets won't be easy. (買票不容易。) (= *Getting tickets will be difficult*.) 可用現在式，寫成：It isn't easy getting tickets. 或 It isn't easy to get tickets.

1-9 Why don't we go *on a weekday*?

　　　weekday 是「平日；工作日」，即週一至週五。

　　　也可説成：Why don't we go during the week? (我們何不平日去？) 或 We should try going during the week. (我們應該平日去。)【try 可以不翻】

星期幾通常用介系詞 on，詳見「文法寶典」p.591。

【比較】 Why don't we go *on Friday*?
　　　　　 (我們何不週五去？)
　　　　　 Why don't we go *some other day*?
　　　　　 (我們何不改天去？)
　　　　　【some other day「改天」，是副詞，不用 on】
　　　　　 Why don't we go *on the weekend*?
　　　　　 (我們何不週末去？)

2. It couldn't be helped.

I'm sorry I *made you wait*.	很抱歉，我讓你久等了。
It couldn't be *helped*.	沒辦法避免。
A traffic jam *prevented* me *from* arriving on time. 【東北學院大】	交通阻塞使我無法準時到達。
I didn't *sleep well*.	我沒睡好。
I *tossed and turned* all night.	我整晚翻來覆去睡不好。
The bed *I slept in* wasn't very comfortable. 【慶大】	我睡的床不是很舒服。
I'm a *responsible* person.	我是個負責任的人。
I'm always *on time*.	我總是很準時。
As far as work is concerned, I always try to do my best. 【大阪產業大】	就工作而言，我總是盡全力。

** ─────────────────

help〔hɛlp〕*v.* 避免　　jam〔dʒæm〕*n.* 阻塞
traffic jam 交通阻塞
prevent…from 阻止…～；使…無法～　　*on time* 準時
toss and turn 翻來覆去睡不好（= *be unable to sleep*）
responsible〔rɪ'spɑnsəbḷ〕*adj.* 負責任的
as far as…is concerned 就…而言　　*do one's best* 盡力

【背景説明】

無論説中文或英文,説好聽的話,人人喜歡。
藉著學英文的機會,説一些禮貌、體貼的話,英
文會説,中文自然而然也會説了。

2-1 I'm sorry I made you wait.
= I'm sorry that I made you wait.

也可説成:I'm sorry for making you wait. (很抱
歉讓你久等了。) 使役動詞 make 後,接原形動詞。

2-2 It couldn't be helped.

句中的 helped 等於 avoided,這句話可説成:It
couldn't be avoided. (沒辦法避免。) It 是指「我遲到」
(My being late) 這件事情,也可説成 It was out of
my control. (這不是我能控制的。) 美國人也常説:
There was nothing I could do about it. (我沒辦法。)

2-3 A traffic jam *prevented* me *from* arriving *on time*.

$$\begin{cases} \textit{prevent}\cdots\textit{from} \quad 阻止\sim \\ = \text{stop}\cdots\text{from} \\ = \text{keep}\cdots\text{from} \end{cases}$$

jam 主要意思是「果醬」,車子擠得和果醬一樣,就
是「交通阻塞」,你看美國人多幽默!

這句話也可簡單説成：I'm late because of the traffic.（我因爲交通阻塞遲到。）也可用假設法，説成：

I would have arrived *on time* **if** *not for the traffic*.

（如果不是因爲交通阻塞，我就會準時到達。）

【if not for　要不是；如果沒有（= *if it had not been for*）】

　　遲到了一定要説出理由，否則會更不禮貌，A bad excuse is better than none at all.（一個勉強的藉口總是沒有好。）

2-4　I didn't sleep *well*.

　　也可説成：I didn't get much sleep last night.
（我昨天沒睡什麼覺。）或 I couldn't sleep last night.
（我昨天晚上沒辦法睡覺。）

2-5　I *tossed and turned all night*.

　　toss 的主要意思是「丟；拋」，toss and turn 是個成語，作「翻來覆去睡不好」解。也可説成：I was unable to sleep all night.（我整晚無法入睡。）或 I slept badly last night.（我昨晚睡得不好。）

2-6　The bed *I slept in* wasn't *very* comfortable.

　　美國人也常説成：The bed I slept in was very uncomfortable.（我睡的床很不舒服。）句中 I slept in 是省略關代 which 的形容詞子句，修飾 The bed。

2-7 I'm a *responsible* person.

也可說成：I take my responsibilities very seriously.
（我是個認眞負責的人。）或 I'm a conscientious person.
（我是負責盡職的人。）
take…seriously 認眞看待…
conscientious〔͵kɑnʃɪˈɛnʃəs〕*adj.* 有良心的；負責盡職的

2-8 I'm *always* on time.
= I'm always on schedule.
= I'm always punctual.

這三句話意思相同。也可說成：I'm never late.
（我從不遲到。）【schedule〔ˈskɛdʒʊl〕*n.* 時間表
on schedule 準時　punctual〔ˈpʌŋktʃʊəl〕*adj.* 準時的】

2-9 *As far as work is concerned, I always* try to do my best.

as far as…is concerned 就…而言；至於

這句話也可說成：As for work, I always try to
do my best.（至於工作，我總是盡力。）句中的 As for
可用 As to 來代替，都作「至於」解。
【do one's best 盡力】

3. I'll be with you.

I'll be *with you*.	我會支持你。
I'll *support* you.	我會支持你。
As long as I live, I will not let you *go hungry*.【立命館大】	只要我還活著，我不會讓你挨餓。
Are you *still* eating?	你還在吃嗎？
It's not *good* for you.	這對你不好。
You can*not* lose weight *until* you give up eating between meals. 【學習院大】	直到你放棄吃零食，你才能減重。
Old habits *die hard*.	積習難改。
Old dogs cannot learn new tricks.	老狗學不會新把戲。
A bad habit, *once formed*, cannot easily be gotten rid of.【青山學院大】	壞習慣一旦養成，就無法輕易戒除。

** ──────────────────

be with sb. 支持某人　　support〔sə'port〕v. 支持

as long as 只要　　go〔go〕v. 處於…狀態

not…until 直到～才…　　*lose weight* 減輕體重

give up 放棄　　meal〔mil〕n. 一餐

eat between meals 吃零食　　*die hard* 難戒除

trick〔trɪk〕n. 把戲　　once〔wʌns〕conj. 一旦

form〔fɔrm〕v. 形成；養成（習慣）　　*get rid of* 除去；擺脫

【背景説明】

兩個短句一個長句最好背，説出來的話又有
力量。要養成習慣，開口説英文時，要一次説三
句以上，越講越多，講多了，英文自然流利。

3-1　I'll be with you.

字面的意思是「我將和你在一起。」引申爲「我會支
持你。」也可説成：I'll be there for you. 或 I'll be by
your side. 意思相同。

3-2　I'll support you.

可加長爲：I'll support you *no matter what*.（我無
論如何都會支持你。）或 I'll support you *through thick
and thin*.（無論艱難困苦，我都會支持你。）

【through thick and thin　在任何情況下；不顧艱難險阻】

3-3　*As long as I live*, I will not let you go hungry.

句中的 go hungry 等於 be hungry。也可説成：
You'll never go hungry as long as I'm around.（只要
有我在，你永遠不會挨餓。）或 As God is my witness,
you'll never starve.（上帝是我的證人，你絕不會挨餓。）

around〔əˋraʊnd〕*adj.* 存在的　　witness〔ˋwɪtnɪs〕*n.* 證人

3-4　Are you *still* eating?

　　　看到你的朋友一直在吃東西，你就可以說這句話勸他。也可說成：Are you eating again?（你又在吃了嗎？）或 You shouldn't be eating right now.（你現在不應該吃。），用進行式加強語氣。

3-5　It's not good *for you*.

　　　也可說成：It's not healthy.（這樣不健康。）或 It's bad for you.（這對你不好。）

3-6　You can*not* lose weight *until you give up eating*

between meals.

not…until　直到～才…

　　　字面的意思是「直到你放棄在兩餐之間吃東西之前，你無法減重。」也就是「直到你放棄吃零食，你才能減重。」也可說成：To lose weight, you must eat only three meals a day.（為了減重，你必須一天只吃三餐。）

　　　這三句是和熟的朋友開玩笑時說，千萬不要對已經很胖的人說，免得對方生氣。

3-7 Old habits die *hard.*

這句話是常用的諺語，die hard 是「難戒除」。也可
說成：Old habits are hard to break. (舊有的習慣很難戒
除。)【break a habit 戒除習慣】

3-8 Old dogs cannot learn new tricks.

這句來自諺語：You cannot teach an old dog
new tricks. (老狗學不會新把戲；朽木不可雕。)

3-9 A bad habit, ***once formed,*** cannot *easily* be gotten
rid of.

form〔fɔrm〕*v.* 形成；養成 (習慣)

get rid of 除去；擺脫

【例】 You must ***get rid of*** a bad habit.【主動】
　　　　　　　　及物動詞片語
　　= A bad habit must ***be gotten rid of.***【被動】
　　　　　　　　　　　　　完全不及物動詞片語

get rid of 是「及物動詞片語」，改成被動後，變成「完
全不及物動詞片語」。

once formed 源自 once it is formed「一旦被形成」，
但在此 it is 必須省略。

UNIT 2 4~6劇情簡介

【拉近關係】

4. ***Call me.***
Contact me.
Should anything happen,
    let me know immediately.

I will.
（我會的。）

I need you.
There is much to be done.
It is essential that you be
    here now.

I'm here now.
（我在這裏。）

Your situation is awful.
Stick with me, the best is yet
    to come.
All things considered, I think
    this is the safest policy.

You're right.
（你說的對。）

* * *

【不想遲到】

5. ***I don't want to be late.***
Let's not take a regular train.
Let's take an express train so that
    we can get there earlier.

OK.
（好。）

Oh, no, we missed it.
The train has left.
If we had arrived earlier, we
    could have caught the train.

Oh well.
(哦，嗯。)

This isn't it.
We got lost somehow.
The place which we are looking
    for is on the main street.

Let's turn ba
(我們回頭吧

* * *

【對一個生氣的人說話】

6. *I'm going to try it.*
    I'm going to give it a shot.
    Whether you agree or not will
        make no difference.

I see.
(我了解。)

Our letter to you was returned.
Our phone call to you went
    unanswered.
Please inform us of any address
    change.

I will do that.
(我會那麼做

I understand why you did it.
I'm not angry with you.
I don't blame you for doing that.

That makes me
feel better.
(讓我覺得好多了

4. Call me.

Call me.	打電話給我。
Contact me.	和我連絡。
Should anything happen, let me know immediately.【拓殖大】	萬一有什麼事發生，要立刻讓我知道。
I need you.	我需要你。
There is much to be done.	有很多事要做。
It is essential that you *be* here now.【拓殖大】	你現在必須來這裡。
Your situation is *awful*.	你的情況很糟。
Stick with me, the best is yet to come.	和我在一起，好事終將來到。
All things considered, this is the safest policy.【愛知工大】	整體看來，這是最安全的方法。

**

call〔kɔl〕v. 打電話給
contact〔'kɑntækt〕v. 和…連絡　　should〔ʃud〕aux. 萬一
immediately〔ɪ'midɪɪtlɪ〕adv. 立刻
essential〔ɪ'sɛnʃəl〕adj. 必要的
situation〔ˌsɪtʃu'eʃən〕n. 情況　　awful〔'ɔfəl〕adj. 糟糕的
stick with sb. 和某人在一起　　yet〔jɛt〕adv. 終將；遲早
all things considered 通盤考量後；整體看來
policy〔'pɑləsɪ〕n. 政策；方法

【背景説明】

先有語言，才有文法規則，文法是語言的歸納，用文法造句很危險，如：***All things considered***，已經成爲固定用法，就不能改回副詞子句的形式，所以，背句子是學英文最簡單的方法。

4-1 Call me.

可加長爲：Call me if you have time.（如果有時間，打個電話給我。）或 Call me when you have a chance.（有機會打個電話給我。）

4-2 Contact me.

可加長爲：Contact me when you can.（可以的話，和我連絡。）也可説成：Get in touch with me.（和我連絡。）【get in touch with 和…連繫】

4-3 *Should anything happen*, let me know *immediately*.

這句話是倒裝句，等於 **If anything should happen,** let me know immediately.（萬一有事情發生，要立刻通知我。）也可説成：Let me know if something should happen.（萬一有什麼事發生，要讓我知道。）

4-4　I need you.

可加強語氣說成：I need you right now.（我現在需要你。）也可說成：I need your help.（我需要你的幫助。）或 Your presence is necessary.（你需要來。）

【presence〔'prɛzn̩s〕*n.* 出席；在場】

4-5　There is much *to be done*.

也可說成：There is a lot of work to do.（有很多工作要做。）或 We have much to do.（我們有很多事要做。）

4-6　It is essential that you *be* here now.

It is
{
essential（必要的）
necessary（需要的）
important（重要的）
}
+ that + S. + (should) + V原

【詳見「文法寶典」p.374】

說話者認為「應該做而未做」，所以用假設法 should + 原形動詞，should 現在美國人多省略。

這句話可簡單說成：You must be here now.（你現在必須來這裡。）

4-7　Your situation is *awful*.

美國人喜歡用 Your situation …，例如：Your situation is *good*.（你的情況很好。）Your situation is *unfortunate*.（你的情況很不幸。）Your situation *is improving*.（你的情況在改善。）

4-8 *Stick with me*, the best is *yet* to come.

> 這句話是慣用句，源自：Stick with me and the best is yet to come.（和我在一起，好事終將來到。）用 "，" 代替 and。yet 在此作「將來某個時候；終將；遲早」解，例如：He may succeed yet.（他遲早會成功。）
>
> 也可說成：Trust me, things are going to get better.（相信我，情況會越來越好。）【慣用句】或 Believe in me, and I won't let you down.（如果你信任我，我不會讓你失望。） things〔θɪŋz〕*n. pl.* 情況 believe in 信任 let sb. down 讓某人失望
>
> 美國人常說：Trust me, you can make it.（相信我，你會成功。）和本句一樣是慣用句。

4-9 *All things considered*, this is the safest policy.

> 雖然 **All things considered** 源自 *After all things are considered*，改成分詞構句，原本應該是 All things being considered，但因為使用頻繁，已經變成慣用語，作「從各方面考慮起來；通盤考量後；整體看來」解。
>
> 【例】 **All things considered**, we did a good job.
> （整體看來，我們做得很好。）
>
> **All things considered**, you made the right choice.（整體看來，你做了正確的選擇。）
>
> *all things being considered* 是對還錯呢？文法上對，但美國人不說，即是錯，因為先有語言才有文法。

5. We got lost somehow.

I don't want to be late.	我不想遲到。
Let's not take a *regular train*.	我們不要坐普通車。
Let's take an express train *so that* we can get there earlier.	我們坐快車，這樣才能早點到那裡。
【七試】	

Oh, no, we missed it.	噢，糟糕，我們沒趕上車。
The train has left.	火車已經離開。
If we *had arrived* earlier, we *could have caught* the train.	如果我們早點到，就能趕上火車了。
【南山大】	

This isn't it.	不是這個地方。
We *got lost* somehow.	不知道為什麼，我們迷路了。
The place *which we are looking for* is on the main street.	我們要找的地方在主要的街上。
【關西學院大】	

**

late〔let〕*adj.* 遲到的　　take〔tek〕*v.* 搭乘
regular〔'rɛgjələ〕*adj.* 普通的
regular train 普通車（= *local train*）
express〔ɪk'sprɛs〕*adj.* 快速的　　*express train* 快車
miss〔mɪs〕*v.* 錯過；沒趕上　　catch〔kætʃ〕*v.* 趕上
get lost 迷路　　somehow〔'sʌm,hau〕*adv.* 不知道為什麼
main〔men〕*adj.* 主要的　　*main street* 主要的街；大街

【背景説明】

迷路的時候説：We got lost. 不能説：*We get lost.* 有時用過去式代替現在式，用有限的文法規則造句，一不小心就會錯。

5-1 I don't want to be late.

可説成：I want to be there on time.（我想要準時到那裡。）【on time 準時】

5-2 Let's not take a regular train.

regular (ˈrɛgjələ) *adj.* 普通的

可説成：A regular train is too slow.（普通車太慢了。）

5-3 Let's take an express train *so that we can get there earlier.*

express 主要意思是「表達」，在此當形容詞用，指「快速的」，express train 指「快車」。

這句話可説成：An express train will get us there earlier.（快車會讓我們早一點到那裡。）或 An express train is so much faster.（快車快多了。）

表「目的」的副詞子句，連接詞有 that, so that, in order that，但在這裡，美國人不習慣使用 that，不是每個句子都可適用文法規則。

5-4　Oh, no, we missed it.

　　　　一般小事情用 Oops〔ups〕*interj.* 哎喲；大事情用
Oh, no!（噢，糟糕！）

　　【例】Oops, I forgot my umbrella.

　　　　　（哎喲，我忘記我的雨傘。）

　　　　　Oh, no!　We're late for class.

　　　　　（噢，糟了！我們上課遲到了。）

　　　　　【詳見「一口氣背會話」p.749】

　　這句話可加強語氣說成：Oh, no, we just missed it.

　　（噢，糟糕，我們剛好沒趕上車。）

5-5　The train has left.

　　　　可說成：The train has departed.（火車已經離開。）

　　或 The train has left the station.（火車已經離開車站。）

　　不可說成：*The train has gone.*（誤）

　　【depart〔dɪ'pɑrt〕*v.* 離開】

**5-6　*If we had arrived earlier*, we could have caught the
train.**

　　　　可倒裝成：Had we arrived earlier, we could have
caught the train.（如果我們早點到達，我們就會趕上這班
火車。）（= *We could have caught the train if we had
arrived earlier.*）會話時能用到假設法的過去式，你說
的話相當有深度，有時美國人都會說錯。

5-7 This isn't it.

> 可説成：This isn't the place. (不是這個地方。)
> 或 This isn't the right place. (這個地方不對。) 如果
> 説：*This is it*. 是指「就是這個地方。」

5-8 We got lost somehow.

> *somehow* 作「不知怎麼地；不知道為什麼」解 (=*for
> some reason you do not know*)。也可説成：Somehow
> we got lost. (不知道為什麼，我們迷路了。) We're lost
> somehow. (不知道為什麼，我們迷路了。)

> *got* 常代替現在式，如：I *got* a problem. (我有個
> 問題。) You *got* it. (你知道該怎麼做。) (= *You know
> what you're doing.*) 美國人避免 got lost 用在現在式，
> 很少用 We *got lost now*. 而常用 We are lost now. (我們
> 現在迷路了。) 因為 got 是過去式動詞，now 是現在，放
> 在一起很奇怪。

5-9 The place *which we are looking for* is on the main
street.

> 可説成：The spot *we are looking for* is on the
> main street. (我們要找的地點在主要的街上。)
> 【spot〔spat〕*n.* 地點】

> 通常一個小鎮都有一條 main street (主要的街；大
> 街)，很多商店都在這條街上。

6. *I understand why you did it.*

I'm going to *try it*.	我要試一試。
I'm going to *give it a shot*.	我要試一試。
Whether you agree or not will *make no difference*.	無論你是否同意都一樣。
【東北工大、松山大】	
Our letter to you was *returned*.	我們寄給你的信被退回了。
Our phone call to you *went unanswered*.	我們打給你的電話沒人接。
Please *inform* us *of* any address change. 【中央大】	如果地址有更改，請通知我們。
I *understand* why you did it.	我了解你爲什麼這麼做。
I'm not angry with you.	我沒生你的氣。
I don't *blame* you *for* doing that. 【關西外大】	我不怪你那麼做。

** ─────────────────

give it a shot 試試看　*whether…or nor* 無論是否…
make no difference 沒有差別；都一樣
return〔rɪˈtɝn〕*v.* 退回　go〔go〕*v.* 處於（某種狀態）
unanswered〔ʌnˈænsəd〕*adj.* 未答應的；未接聽的
inform〔ɪnˈfɔrm〕*v.* 通知
inform sb. of sth. 通知某人某事　address〔əˈdrɛs〕*n.* 地址
be angry with sb. 對某人生氣　blame〔blem〕*v.* 責備

【背景説明】

在大規模考試中，往往有很多好的句子，如
I don't blame you for doing that.，加上兩個短
句，以三句爲一組，背完之後，要不斷使用，成
爲自己的語言。

6-1　I'm going to try it.

可説成：I'll give it a try. (我要試一試。)
(= *I'll try it.*) 【give it a try　試試看】

6-2　I'm going to give it a shot.

give it a shot (試試看)，源自投籃。也可説成：
I'll give it a shot. (我要試一試。)

6-3　<u>Whether you agree or not</u> will make no difference.
　　　　　名　詞　子　句

也可説成：It makes no difference whether you
agree or not. (你是否同意都一樣。) 或 I don't care
whether you agree with me or not. (我不在乎你是否同
意我。) 【care〔kɛr〕v. 在乎】

6-4　Our letter *to you* was returned.

　　　也可説成：You didn't receive our letter.（你沒有

收到我們的信。）或 Our letter to you was not received.

（我們寄給你的信你沒收到。）

6-5　Our phone call *to you* went unanswered.
　　　　　　　　　　　　　was

　　　可説成：You didn't answer our call.（你沒有接我

們的電話。）或 We were unable to reach you by phone.

（我們無法用電話連絡到你。）

answer〔'ænsɚ〕*v.* 接（電話）

reach〔ritʃ〕*v.* 連絡到（某人）

6-6　Please inform us of any address change.

***inform** sb. **of** sth.* 通知某人某事

　　　可説成：Please let us know if you have moved.

（如果你搬家，請通知我們。）【move〔muv〕*v.* 搬家】

6-7　I understand <u>why you did it</u>.
　　　　　　　　名 詞 子 句

　　　看到別人生氣，就要講這句話。可説成：I see why

you did it.（我了解你爲什麼這麼做。）或 Your actions

are understandable.（你的行爲我能了解。）

【see〔si〕*v.* 知道；了解】

6-8　I'm not angry with you.

也可説成：I'm not upset with you.（我沒生你的氣。）或 I'm not unhappy with you.（我不會對你不高興。）【upset〔ʌp'sɛt〕adj. 生氣的】

6-9　I don't blame you for doing that.

可説成：You are not to blame.（你不該受責備。）（= You are not to be blamed.）【詳見「文法寶典」p.425】或 It's not your fault.（不是你的錯。）

【fault〔fɔlt〕n. 過錯】

> 有一次，我的同事 Christian 爲了某件事情很生氣，我就跟他説：
>
> I understand why you did it.
> I'm not angry with you.
> I don't blame you for doing that.
>
> 説話是一種藝術，藉著學英文的機會，學習説讓別人聽起來舒服的話，可化危機爲轉機，關鍵的話一句可抵一萬句。英文學會了，中文也會因而改善。

UNIT 2　7~9劇情簡介

【勸人買東西，不要浪費】

7. ***Here is some good advice.***
   Learn something new every day.
   Now that you are in Taipei,
   　you should do some shopping.

I plan on it.
（我計畫這麼做。）

Buy what you need.
Don't buy what you want.
I didn't buy anything because
　I didn't see what I needed.

That's the
way to be.
（這樣就對了。）

Simple pleasures are the best.
I'm a frugal person.
Poor as I am, I live happily.

Good for you.
（你真行。）

* * *

【變天帶傘；安全至上】

8. ***It's getting late.***
   Traffic will be light.
   It's time we left now.

Let's go.
（走吧。）

The weather can turn bad in
　　the blink of an eye.
Better safe than sorry.
I think we had better carry
　　an umbrella in case it rains.

I have one here.
（我這有一把。）

Let's ask someone for help.
I don't feel comfortable here.
We don't know the area, and
　　what is worse, we can't
　　find our hotel.

I'm scared.
（我嚇到了。）

* * *

【交友須慎重，不貳過】

9. *He is a disappointment.*
He cannot tell right from
　　wrong.
I regarded him as a friend
　　but he betrayed me.

He's a bad guy.
（他是壞人。）

I'm done with him.
I don't need an apology.
It doesn't matter whether he
　　admits his guilt or not.

Suit yourself.
（隨你便。）

Choose your friends wisely.
Be a good judge of character.
Don't make the same mistake I made.

I won't.
（我不會。）

7. *Simple pleasures are the best*.

Here is some good *advice*.	我有一些好的勸告給你。
Learn something new every day.	每天都要學習新東西。
Now that you are in Taipei, you should do some shopping.	既然你在台北，你應該去買些東西。
【東京國際大】	

Buy what you need.	買你需要的東西。
Don't buy what you want.	不要買你想要的東西。
I didn't buy anything *because* I didn't see what I needed. 【別府大】	我什麼也沒買，因為我沒看到我需要的東西。

Simple pleasures are *the best*.	往往最好的快樂最簡單。
I'm a *frugal* person.	我很節儉。
Poor as I am, I live happily.	雖然我很窮，但我過得
【東京國際大】	很快樂。

**

advice〔əd'vaɪs〕*n.* 勸告　　***now that*** 既然
do some shopping 去買東西 (= *go shopping*)
pleasure〔'plɛʒɚ〕*n.* 快樂的事；樂趣
frugal〔'frugl̩〕*adj.* 節儉的　　as〔æz〕*conj.* 雖然
***Poor as I am*, …** 雖然我很窮，…

【背景説明】

　　　　每天晚上睡覺前，要問自己，有沒有學到什
麼新東西，有沒有做一件好事，如果做到，你會
非常快樂。

7-1　Here is some good advice.

　　　可説成：I have some advice for you.（我有一些勸
告給你。）或 I have some suggestions for you.（我有
一些建議給你。）advice 是抽象名詞，不可數。也可簡
單地説：Take my advice.（聽我的勸告。）

7-2　Learn something *new every day.*

　　　美國人也常説：Try something new every day.
（每天嘗試一些新東西。）或 Try learning something
every day.（每天努力學一些新東西。）

7-3　*Now that you are in Taipei,* you should do some shopping.

　　　可説成：As long as you are in Taipei, you should
do some shopping.（只要你在台北，你應該去買些東西。）
或 You should do some shopping now that you are in
Taipei.（既然你在台北，你應該去買些東西。）

now that 因為；既然（= *since*），now that 在口語中，
常把 that 省略，只用 now 當連接詞。【詳見「文法寶典」
p.510】

> *do some shopping* 去購物
> = do *one's* shopping
> = go shopping

7-4 Buy <u>what you need</u>.
　　　　 名　詞　子　句

可加強語氣說成：Buy only what you need.（只買
你所需要的東西。）(= *Only buy what's necessary.*)

7-5 Don't buy <u>what you want</u>.
　　　　 名　詞　子　句

可說成：Don't buy on impulse.（不要因為衝動買
東西。）【impulse〔'ɪmpʌls〕*n.* 衝動　　on impulse 衝動
之下】或 Don't buy something just because you
want it.（不要因為你想要而買。）

7-6 I didn't buy anything *because I didn't see what I needed.*

可說成：I didn't see what I needed, so I didn't
buy anything.（我沒看到我需要的東西，所以我什麼也
沒買。）

7-7 Simple pleasures are the best.

也可説成：The best things in life are free. (人生
當中最美好的事物是免費的。) 人生中的快樂往往很簡單，
如喝一杯好的咖啡 (a good cup of coffee)、看到美麗
的日落 (a beautiful sunset)，或和你喜歡的人在公園
散步 (a walk in the park with a loved one)。

無論做什麼事，越簡單越好。美國人也常説：
The simple way is the best way. (方法越簡單越好。)
Simple pleasures are the best pleasures. (往往最好的
快樂最簡單。)

7-8 I'm a frugal person.
frugal〔'frugḷ〕 *adj.* 節儉的

也可説成：I'm very frugal. 或 I'm very thrifty.
(我很節儉。)【thrifty〔'θrɪftɪ〕 *adj.* 節儉的】

7-9 *Poor **as** I am*, I live *happily*.
= Although I am poor, I live happily.

as 在第二個字，作「雖然」解。這句話也可説成：
Even though I am poor, I live well. (雖然我很窮，但
我過得很好。) 或 I live happily, even though I am
poor. (即使我很窮，我還是過得很快樂。)

8. *Traffic will be light.*

It's *getting late*.	時間越來越晚了。
Traffic will be *light*.	交通不會繁忙。
It's time we *left* now. 【東洋大】	我們現在該走了。
The weather can turn bad *in the blink of an eye*.	天氣可能一眨眼就變壞了。
Better safe than sorry.	安全總比後悔好。
I think we had better carry an umbrella *in case* it rains. 【東邦大】	我認爲我們最好帶把傘，以防萬一下雨。
Let's *ask* someone *for* help.	我們請人幫忙吧。
I don't *feel comfortable* here.	我在這裡覺得不舒服。
We don't know the area, *and what is worse*, we can't find our hotel. 【立命館大】	我們對這一區不熟，更糟的是，找不到我們的旅館。

**

traffic〔'træfɪk〕*n.* 交通流量
light〔laɪt〕*adj.*（量）輕微的
It's time ~ . 是該…的時候了。
turn〔tɝn〕*v.* 轉變成　　blink〔blɪŋk〕*n.* 眨眼
in the blink of an eye 瞬間；一眨眼功夫
sorry〔'sɔrɪ〕*adj.* 後悔的　　*had better* 最好
in case 以防萬一　　area〔'ɛrɪə〕*n.* 地區
what is worse 更糟的是

【背景説明】

　　「一口氣考試英語」每一句都經過精挑細選，
背到變成直覺後，你説的英文會比美國人好，使他
們很佩服，自己越説會越有信心。

8-1　It's getting late.

　　　也可説成：The hour is late. (時間很晚了。) 或 It's
late. (很晚了。)【hour〔aʊr〕*n.* 時間】

8-2　Traffic will be light.

　　　light 主要意思是「光線」，在此當「輕的；少量的」解。
這句話可説成：Traffic will not be heavy. (交通不會繁忙。)
或 The roads won't be congested. (道路不會阻塞。)
heavy〔'hɛvɪ〕*adj.* 大量的　　congest〔kən'dʒɛst〕*v.* 使阻塞
traffic 通常不加冠詞，除了限定以外，如：The traffic
in Taipei isn't too bad. (台北的交通不會太差。)

8-3　It's time we left now.
　　　It's time
　　　It's about time 〕+ S. + 過去式 V. 是該⋯的時候了
　　　It's high time 〕【詳見「文法寶典」p.374】

　　　用過去式動詞，表示「與過去事實相反」，現在極
少用 should + 原形 V.。也可説成：We should go now.
(我們現在應該走。) 或 Let's get moving. (我們走吧。)

※ 爲什麼 It's time we *left* now. 常考？
　因爲很特殊，是用假設法動詞 left，表「與現在事實
　相反」，照理説可用 should leave 或原形動詞 leave，
　但現在極少用，只用過去式動詞。

8-4　The weather can turn bad *in the blink of an eye.*

turn bad 變壞　　blink〔blɪŋk〕*n.* 眨眼

in the blink of an eye 瞬間；一眨眼功夫（= *very quickly*）

美國人也常說：The weather is changeable.（天氣多變化。）或 The weather is unpredictable.（天氣變化莫測。）【unpredictable〔͵ʌnprɪˈdɪktəbl̩〕*adj.* 無法預測的】

8-5　Better safe than sorry.

這句話是慣用句，字典上查不到，源自 It is better to be safe than sorry.（安全總比後悔好。）【詳見「一口氣背會話」p.453】也可說成：It is better to be safe now than sorry later on.（現在安全比以後後悔好。）

【***later on*** 以後】

8-6　I think we had better carry an umbrella *in case*

it rains.

in case 以防萬一；如果【可表「條件」，也可表「否定的結果」，詳見「文法寶典」p.514, 525】

可說成：… in case it should rain. 還可說成：In case it rains, bring an umbrella.（帶把傘，以防萬一下雨。）（= *In case it should rain, bring an umbrella.*）

8-7　Let's ask someone for help.

　　　　「請求某人做某事」用 ask *sb*. for *sth*.，這句話可簡化爲：Let's ask for help.（我們請別人幫助吧。）或 Let's ask for assistance.（我們請求別人協助吧。）【assistance〔ə'sɪstəns〕*n.* 協助】

8-8　I don't feel comfortable here.

　　　　可說成：I don't feel safe here.（我覺得這裡不安全。）或 This place makes me nervous.（這個地方使我緊張。）【nervous〔'nɜvəs〕*adj.* 緊張的】

8-9　We don't know the area, *and what is worse*, we can't find the hotel.

　　　　可說成：We don't know our way around, and we can't find the hotel.（我們對附近不熟，而且找不到旅館。）【know one's way around　熟悉（某處的）地理環境】

what is worse　更糟的是	
what is better　更好的是	都是「插入語」。
what is more　此外；而且	

　　　在口語中學會用 what is worse，你的英文會更讓人佩服。如：Traffic is heavy, *and what is worse*, it's raining cats and dogs.（車子很多，更糟的是，雨又下得很大。）

9. I'm done with him.

He is a *disappointment*.
他令人失望。

He cannot *tell* right *from*
wrong. 【九州國際大】
他無法分辨對錯。

I *regarded* him *as* a friend but
he betrayed me. 【駒澤大】
我認為他是朋友，但是他
卻背叛我。

I'*m done with* him.
我和他完了。

I don't need an apology.
我不需要他的道歉。

It doesn't matter whether he
admits his guilt or not.
　　【高岡法科大】
他是否認錯都一樣。

Choose your friends wisely.
要聰明地選擇朋友。

Be a good judge of character.
要善於判斷一個人的性格。

Don't make the same mistake
I made.
不要和我犯同樣的錯誤。

** ─────────────

disappointment〔,dɪsə'pɔɪntmənt〕n. 令人失望的人或物
tell〔tɛl〕v. 分辨　　*tell right from wrong* 分辨是非
regard A as B 認為 A 是 B　　betray〔bɪ'tre〕v. 背叛；出賣
be done with sb. 與某人斷絕關係　　apology〔ə'pɑlədʒɪ〕n. 道歉
it doesn't matter 沒關係　　guilt〔gɪlt〕n. 罪；過錯
wisely〔'waɪzlɪ〕adv. 聰明地　　judge〔dʒʌdʒ〕n. 鑑賞家；裁判
be a good judge of sth. 善於判斷～
character〔'kærɪktɚ〕n. 性格；人格

【背景説明】

用文法規則造句，會使自己陷於狹窄的範圍，説起話來與美國人所説的話格格不入。句子背多了，每個句子像是一個句型，可無限發揮。

9-1 He is a disappointment.

這個句子真好，不背你怎麼會説？原來 disappointment 還可當「使人失望的人或事」解。

> 【例】 He was a ***disappointment*** to his parents.
>
> （他使父母失望。）
>
> The movie was a ***disappointment***.
>
> （這部電影令人失望。）
>
> Her performance was a ***disappointment***.
>
> （她的表現令人失望。）

也可説成：He disappointed me. (他令我失望。)

(= *He let me down.*)

9-2 He cannot ***tell*** right *from* wrong.

= He does not know right from wrong.

$$\begin{cases} \textbf{\textit{tell}} \ A \ \textbf{\textit{from}} \ B \quad 分辨 \ A \ 與 \ B \\ = know \ A \ from \ B \end{cases}$$

也可説成：He doesn't know the difference between right and wrong. (他無法分辨是非。)

9-3　I regarded him as a friend but he betrayed me.

> ***regard*** A ***as*** B　認為 A 是 B
> = think of A as B
> = refer to A as B
> = look upon A as B
>
> = see A as B
> = view A as B
> = treat A as B
> = consider A (to be) B

可説成：I considered him a friend, but he lied to me. (我把他當作朋友，但他騙了我。)

【consider〔kən'sɪdɚ〕*v.* 認為　　lie〔laɪ〕*v.* 說謊】

9-4　I'm done with him.

be done with *sb.* 與某人斷絕關係 (= *be finished with sb.*)

美國人也常説：I don't want to see him anymore. (我不想再見他) 或 I don't want anything to do with him. (我不想要和他有任何關係。)

not…anymore　不再…

have anything to do with　和…有任何關係

9-5　I don't need an apology.

可加長爲：I don't need an apology from him. (我不需要他的道歉。) 也可説成：I don't need to hear an apology from him. (我不需要聽他道歉。)

9-6 It doesn't matter ***whether** he admits his guilt **or not***.

　　　　　　　　　　　　名　　詞　　子　　句

也可説成：It makes no difference whether he admits his guilt or not. (他認不認錯都一樣。) (= *Whether he admits his guilt or not makes no difference to me.*)

9-7 Choose your friends *wisely*.

可加長爲：Choose your friends wisely, or you will suffer the consequences. (選擇朋友要聰明，否則你就要承受後果。)【suffer〔ˈsʌfɚ〕v. 遭受；忍受 consequences〔ˈkɑnsə͵kwɛnsɪz〕n. pl. 後果】

9-8 Be a good judge of character.

源自：Be a good judge of your friend's character. (要懂得判斷你朋友的人格。) judge 在此是名詞，指「鑑賞家；評審」，***be a good judge of*** 則是「善於判斷…」。

9-9 Don't make the same mistake *I made*.

這句話源自 Don't make the same mistake that I made. 關代 that 可省略。【詳見「文法寶典」p.127】

也可説成：Don't follow my example. (不要跟我學。) 或 Avoid making the same mistake. (不要犯同樣的錯。)

follow〔ˈfɑlo〕v. 仿效　　example〔ɪgˈzæmpl̩〕n. 榜樣
follow one's example　學習某人的榜樣；以某人爲榜樣

一口氣考試英語 Unit 2

※ 以三組爲一個單位較好背。

1. *Our work is done*.
   Now, we can *relax*.
   It's such a lovely day that
     everybody *feels like going* out.
   【東京經濟大】

   I don't *read much*.
   Watching movies is like a kind
     of reading to me.
   Reading is to the mind *what*
     exercise is to the body. 【駒澤大】

   It being Sunday, the theater
     will be crowded. 【北海學園大】
   It won't be easy *getting tickets*.
   Why don't we go *on a weekday*?

2. I'm sorry I *made you wait*.
   It couldn't be *helped*.
   A traffic jam *prevented* me *from*
     arriving on time. 【東北學院大】

   I didn't *sleep well*.
   I *tossed and turned* all night.
   The bed *I slept in* wasn't very
     comfortable. 【慶大】

   I'm a *responsible* person.
   I'm always *on time*.
   As far as work is concerned, I
     always try to do my best. 【大阪產業大】

3. I'll be *with you*.
   I'll *support* you.
   As long as I live, I will not let you
   go hungry. 【立命館大】

Are you *still* eating?
It's not *good* for you.
You can*not* lose weight *until*
  you give up eating between
  meals. 【學習院大】

Old habits *die hard*.
Old dogs cannot learn new
  tricks.
A bad habit, *once formed*,
  cannot easily be gotten rid
  of. 【青山學院大】

*   *   *

4. *Call me*.
   Contact me.
   Should anything happen, let
     me know immediately. 【拓殖大】

   I need you.
   There is much to be done.
   It is essential that you *be* here
     now. 【拓殖大】

   Your situation is *awful*.
   Stick with me, the best is yet
     to come.
   All things considered, I think
     this is the safest policy.
   【愛知工大】

5. I don't want to be late.
   Let's not take a *regular train*.
   Let's take an express train *so
     that* we can get there earlier.
   【七試】

Oh, *no*, we missed it.

The train has left.

If we *had arrived* earlier, we *could have caught* the train. 【南山大】

This isn't it.

We *got lost* somehow.

The place *which we are looking for* is on the main street. 【關西學院大】

6. I'm going to *try it*.

I'm going to *give it a shot*.

Whether you agree or not will *make no difference*.

【東北工大、松山大】

Our letter to you was *returned*.

Our phone call to you *went unanswered*.

Please *inform* us *of* any address change. 【中央大】

I *understand* why you did it.

I'm not angry with you.

I don't *blame* you *for* doing that.

【關西外大】

*　　　*　　　*

7. *Here is some good advice*.

Learn something new every day.

Now that you are in Taipei, you should do some shopping.

【東京國際大】

Buy what you need.

Don't buy what you want.

I didn't buy anything *because* I didn't see what I needed. 【別府大】

Simple pleasures are *the best*.

I'm a *frugal* person.

Poor as I am, I live happily.

【東京國際大】

8. It's *getting late*.

Traffic will be *light*.

It's time we *left* now. 【東洋大】

The weather can turn bad *in the blink of an eye*.

Better safe than sorry.

I think we had better carry an umbrella *in case* it rains.

【東邦大】

Let's *ask* someone *for* help.

I don't *feel comfortable* here.

We don't know the area, *and what is worse*, we can't find our hotel. 【立命館大】

9. He is a *disappointment*.

He cannot *tell* right *from* wrong. 【九州國際大】

I *regarded* him *as* a friend but he betrayed me. 【駒澤大】

I*'m done with* him.

I don't need an apology.

It doesn't matter whether he admits his guilt or not.

【高岡法科大】

Choose your friends wisely.

Be a good judge of character.

Don't make the same mistake I made.

※ 可將這兩頁用手機拍下來背。

你會說 "It being Sunday" 嗎？

　　英文看起來容易，有規則性，但我發現，學起來非常困難，連美國人都學不好，例如，我們在「一口氣考試英語班」中教到：As it is Sunday, the theater will be crowded.（因為是禮拜天，電影院會很擁擠。）改成分詞構句，就變成：*It being Sunday*, the theater will be crowded. 在考試中同學大多都會，可是用在會話中，很少人會說 *It being Sunday*, the theater…。背一句話很辛苦，改成「一口氣英語」的方式，就變簡單了。

> ***It being Sunday***, the theater will be crowded.
> 【日本北海學園大】
> It won't be easy ***getting tickets***.（不容易買到票。）
> Why don't we go ***on a weekday***?（我們何不平日去？）

　　一般人會 It's not easy ***to get tickets***.，卻忽略動名詞 ***getting tickets*** 也可當真正主詞，也常忽略這句話可使用未來式 It won't be…，這三句話背熟，每天都用得到，一個句子代表一個句型，可舉一反三，但是要背過才安全。

> ***It being the weekend***,
> ***It being a weekend***,
> ***It being a holiday***,　＞ the theater will be crowded.
> ***It being the holidays***,
> *It being the holiday*,（誤）

　　我們背了 It being Sunday, the theater will be crowded.，Sunday 是專有名詞，所以不加冠詞，但「週末」要說 the weekend 或 a weekend，那 holiday「假日」呢？不能用 *It being the holiday*（誤）。一天的假期要用 a holiday，二天以上要用 the holidays。光是冠詞，就有人寫了一本一千多頁的書，這樣研究下去怎麼得了！

應徵工作時常講這三句話：

> I'm a responsible person.（我是個負責任的人。）
> I'm always on time.（我總是很準時。）
> *As far as* work *is concerned*, I always try to do
> my best.【日本大阪產業大】
> （就工作而言，我總是盡全力。）

as far as…is concerned 指「就…而言」，這個成語常考，但是如果把 work 改成 job 就錯了，要說成 my job，因為 work 指「工作」，是不可數名詞，而 job 是普通名詞，要加冠詞或所有格。

> As far as *work* is concerned, ….【正】
> As far as *my work* is concerned, ….【正】
> As far as *job* is concerned, ….【誤】
> As far as *my job* is concerned, ….【正】

　　研究起來太複雜了，那我們該怎麼學呢？有人用情境教學，到醫院、到機場、到餐廳，塑造英語環境，我經過 40 幾年教學，覺得統統沒用，因為你背了郵局的對話，你什麼時候才有機會在郵局講呢？學得不確實、模模糊糊，很快就忘記了。英文要求很嚴謹，上面所舉的例子，少一個 the，少一個 s 就錯。美國人說的話並不能寫出來，常常時態會錯誤，尤其是假設法，我們用「一口氣英語」的背誦方式，背的每一句都正確，所以**無論說出來或寫出來，都讓外國人震撼**。背書有很多好處，①**能增強記憶力**，刺激腦細胞活化。任何東西不用就浪費，大腦也是一樣，剛開始背很吃力，越背就會越快。②**不會無聊，永無煩惱**。心情不好的時候背一背，就像念經一樣百毒不侵。③**越背越多，每天都很充實，有成就感**。④有一個說話結巴的人，背 10 分鐘後立刻改善，一位有台中口音的同學，背完後，國語說得像新聞主播，明明是背英文，怎麼國語變好了？我們嘴部的發音肌肉，不說話也會退化，英文唸多了，等於鍛鍊了發音肌肉，說起話來自然流利。

劉毅

UNIT 3　1~3劇情簡介

【遇到朋友很驚喜，邀約對方】

1. ***What a nice surprise!***
   I can't believe my eyes.
   Little did I dream of seeing
    you here.

Nice to see you.
（很高興見到你。）

What are you doing on Sunday?
Come stay with us, won't you?
Let's go hiking, shall we?

Sounds good.
（聽起來不錯。）

You can ride a bike anywhere.
You can rent a bike by the
 hour.
There are bicycle paths all
 around the city.

I didn't know that.
（那個我不知道。）

*   *   *

【想參加校園徵才，媽媽不捨】

2. ***There is a job fair on***
   campus today.
   Many students will be attending.
   I'm going as well.

Have fun.
（好好玩。）

Mother held me by the arm.
She patted me on the shoulder.
She didn't want me to leave.

She loves you
very much.
（她非常愛你。）

I like wearing black clothing.
She prefers to dress in red.
I put on a vest when it gets cold.

I prefer a coat.
（我比較喜歡
穿外套。）

＊　＊　＊

【和朋友分享消息】

3. *Got a minute?*
   You need to hear this.
   I have an interesting piece
      of information.

Let's hear it.
（我們來聽聽看。）

Pandas are rare animals.
They are endangered.
Those who hunt pandas in
   China face the death
   penalty if caught.

The laws are
very strict.
（法律很嚴格。）

Tom burned the candle at both ends.
Then he got sick.
Only when you lose your health will
   you realize how important it is.

Sad but true.
（令人難過但
確實如此。）

1. *What are you doing on Sunday?*

What a nice surprise!	眞令人驚喜！
I can't believe my eyes.	我無法相信我的眼睛。
Little did I dream of seeing you here. 【駒澤大】	我做夢也沒想到會在這裡看到你。
What are you doing *on* Sunday? 【帝塚山學院大】	你禮拜天要做什麼？
Come stay with us, *won't you*? 【東海大】	來和我們一起住，好嗎？
Let's go hiking, *shall we*? 【東洋大】	我們去走走路，好嗎？
You can ride a bike anywhere.	你可以騎腳踏車去任何地方。
You can rent a bike *by the hour*. 【姬路獨協大】	你可以按小時租腳踏車。
There are bicycle paths all around the city.	整個城市到處都有腳踏車專用道。

** ————————————————

dream of 夢想到　　stay〔ste〕*v.* 暫住
hike〔haɪk〕*v.* 健行；徒步旅行；遠足
shall〔ʃəl〕*aux.* 要不要…；…好嗎
bike〔baɪk〕*n.* 腳踏車（= *bicycle*）
anywhere〔'ɛnɪˌhwɛr〕*adv.* 到任何地方　　rent〔rɛnt〕*v.* 租
by the hour 按小時計　　path〔pæθ〕*n.* 通道；路徑
bicycle path 腳踏車專用道　　around〔ə'raʊnd〕*prep.* 在…到處

【背景説明】

英語會話中，最難學的，就是「句尾附加句」。背完這一回九句，你和外國人講話，就會使用「句尾附加句」了。

1-1 What a nice surprise!

這句話是感歎句，源自：What a nice surprise *it is*！（真令人驚喜！）可簡化成：*What a surprise!*（真令人驚訝！）美國人也常説成：*What a pleasant surprise!* 或 *What a wonderful surprise!*，意思相同。

【pleasant〔'plɛznt〕*adj.* 令人愉快的】

1-2 I can't believe my eyes.

美國人也常説成：I can't believe what I'm seeing.（我無法相信我看到的。）可簡化成：*I can't believe it.*（我無法相信。）

1-3 *Little* did I dream of seeing you here.

這句話是倒裝句：「否定字 + 助動詞 + S + V.」，Little 加助動詞時，Little = Not at all = Never。

dream of 夢想到

如果不倒裝，就變成：I never dreamed of seeing you here.（我從來沒夢想到會在這裡見到你。）

美國人也常説成：I didn't expect to see you here.

（我沒想到會在這裡見到你。）【expect〔ɪk'spɛkt〕v. 預期】

1-4　What are you doing *on Sunday*?

字面的意思是「禮拜天你要做什麼？」含有兩個意思：
①你禮拜天有什麼計劃？（= *Do you have any plans for Sunday?*）②禮拜天你忙嗎？（= *Are you busy on Sunday?*），暗示「禮拜天你有空嗎？」（= *Are you free on Sunday?*）

1-5　Come stay *with us*, won't you?

命令句的「句尾附加句」用 ***won't you*** 表「邀請」，是：***won't you*** *come stay with us*? 的省略。

當然可説成：Won't you come stay with us?（你不來和我們一起住嗎？）或 You're welcome to stay with us.（歡迎你和我們一起住。）【詳見「文法寶典」p.6】

1-6　Let's go hiking, shall we?

shall we? 是 ***shall we*** *go hiking*? 的省略，Let's 後面用 shall we 表「提議」。Let us 後面用 ***will you***，表「請求」，如 Let us go, ***will you***?（讓我們走，好嗎？）will you? 是 will you *let us go*? 的省略。

可說成：How about going for a hike?（去走走路如何？）hike 通常是動詞，在此是名詞，一般翻成「健行」。【How about~? ~如何？】go hiking 的用法詳見「一口氣背會話」p.611。

1-7 You can ride a bike *anywhere*.

可說成：You can ride a bike everywhere.（你可以騎腳踏車四處走。）或 With a bike, you can ride wherever you want.（有腳踏車，你可以騎去任何你想去的地方。）

1-8 You can rent a bike *by the hour*.

「by the + 單位名詞」表「按~計」。美國人也常說：Bikes can be rented by the hour.（腳踏車可以按小時租。）或 Bikes are available for rent.（有腳踏車可以租。）

【available〔ə'veləbḷ〕*adj.* 可獲得的　rent〔rɛnt〕*v. n.* 租】

1-9 There are *bicycle* paths *all around the city*.

美國人也常說：The city has many bike paths.（這個城市有很多腳踏車專用道。）

在此 all around the city 可說成 all over the city。

2. *I'm going as well.*

There is a job fair *on campus* today.	今天有校園徵才。
Many students will be *attending*.	許多學生會去參加。
I'm going *as well*. 【九州共立大】	我也會去。
Mother held me *by the* arm. 【流通經濟大】	媽媽抓住我的手臂。
She patted me *on the* shoulder.	她輕拍我的肩膀。
She didn't want me to leave.	她不想要我離開。
I like *wearing* black clothing. 【聖學院大】	我喜歡穿黑色衣服。
She prefers to *dress* in red. 【聖學院大】	她比較喜歡穿紅色的衣服。
I *put on* a vest when it gets cold.	天氣變冷時，我會穿上背心。

**

fair〔fɛr〕*n.* 展覽會　　campus〔'kæmpəs〕*n.* 校園
attend〔ə'tɛnd〕*v.* 參加；出席　　*as well* 也 (= *too*)
pat〔pæt〕*v.* 輕拍　　clothing〔'kloðɪŋ〕*n.* 衣服 (= *clothes*)
prefer〔prɪ'fɝ〕*v.* 比較喜歡
dress〔drɛs〕*v.* 穿　　*dress in red* 穿紅色的衣服
put on 穿上　　vest〔vɛst〕*n.* 背心

【背景說明】

　　文法規則無限多，自己造句無法造出 Many students will be attending. 這種句子，背句子是學英文唯一的捷徑，快又有效。

2-1 There is a job fair *on campus* today.

campus〔ˈkæmpəs〕 *n.* 校園；校區；學校

　　也可說：There is a job fair at school today.（今天學校裡有校園徵才。）fair 當形容詞時，指「公平的；美麗的」，當名詞時，為「展覽會」之意，如 a book fair「書展」，a job fair「就業博覽會」（= *a career fair*）。也可用未來式，說成：There will be a job fair on campus today.（今天學校裡將有校園徵才。）所以說，today 不一定只能用現在式，也可用未來式。

2-2 Many students will be *attending*.

　　attend〔əˈtɛnd〕 *v.* 參加；出席，是及物、不及物兩用動詞，這句話等於：Many students will be attending the fair.（很多學生都會參加此次博覽會。）未來式和未來進行式，都可以表「未來」。

【比較】 Many students will attend. 【一般語氣】
　　　　 Many students will be attending. 【語氣較強】
　　　　　　　　 【詳見「文法寶典」p.348】

這句話也可簡單說成：Many students will be there.
（很多學生會去那裡。）

2-3　I'm going *as well*.

　　as well 作「也」解，等於 too。如：If you go, I'll go *as well*.（如果你要去，那我也會去。）或 He made many mistakes *as well*.（他也犯了許多錯。）

　　這句話也可說成：I'm going too.（我也會去。）(= *I'll be there too*.)

2-4　Mother *held* me *by the* arm.

　　動詞＋某人＋介＋*the*＋某人身體一部分
　　(the 不可改成所有格)【詳見「文法寶典」p.277】

　　可說成：Mother grabbed me by the arm.（媽媽抓住我的手臂。）(= *Mother held on to my arm*.)
　　【hold on to 抓住】

　　現代美語中，可直接說：Mother held my arm.

2-5　She *patted* me *on the* shoulder.

　　可說成：She patted my shoulder.（她輕拍我的肩膀。）或 She gently touched my shoulder.(= *She gently touched me on the shoulder*.)
　　【gently〔ˈdʒɛntḷɪ〕*adv.* 溫和地；輕輕地】

2-6　She didn't want me to leave.

　　可說成：She didn't want me to go.（她不想要我走。）或 She wanted me to stay.（她要我留下來。）

2-7 I like wearing black clothing.

「穿衣服」的説法有：
- wear, dress
- put on【強調動作】

這句話也可説成：I love wearing black clothing.

（我愛穿黑色衣服。）(= *I love wearing black clothes.*)

2-8 She prefers to *dress* in red.

= She prefers to *dress herself* in red.

= She prefers to *be dressed* in red.

（她比較喜歡穿紅色的衣服。）

dress 是及物和不及物兩用動詞，

- dress *v.* 穿衣服
- = dress oneself
- = be dressed

She is dressing now.（她現在正在穿衣服。）

= She is dressing herself now.

= She is getting dressed now.

【不可説成：*She is being dressed now.*（句意不合）】

這句話意思是「她正在讓別人幫她穿衣服。」

2-9 I put on a vest *when it gets cold.*

可説成：When it gets cold, I put on a vest.（天氣變冷時，我會穿上背心。）(= *I put on a vest when the temperature drops.*)

3. Got a minute?

Got a minute?	你有空嗎？
You need to hear this.	你得聽聽這個。
I have *an interesting piece of* information. 【ㄚ試】	我有一個有趣的消息。
Pandas are rare animals.	貓熊是稀有動物。
They are endangered.	牠們瀕臨絕種。
Those who hunt pandas in China face the death penalty *if caught*. 【慶大】	在中國，凡是獵殺貓熊的人，如果被抓到，會面臨死刑。
Tom *burned the candle at both ends*.	湯姆過分透支體力。
Then he got sick.	後來他就生病了。
Only when you lose your health *will you* realize how important it is. 【京都外語大】	唯有失去健康，你才會了解健康有多重要。

** ——————————————

a minute 瞬間；片刻　　*a piece of* 一個；一件
panda (ˈpændə) *n.* 貓熊；熊貓　　rare (rɛr) *adj.* 罕見的；稀有的
endangered (ɪnˈdendʒəd) *adj.* 瀕臨絕種的
hunt (hʌnt) *v.* 獵殺　　face (fes) *v.* 面臨
penalty (ˈpɛnḷtɪ) *n.* 刑罰　　*death penalty* 死刑
candle (ˈkændḷ) *n.* 蠟燭　　end (ɛnd) *n.* 一頭；一端
realize (ˈrɪəlˌaɪz) *v.* 知道；了解

【背景説明】

我常聽外國人説 Got a minute? You need
to hear this. 光聽別人説，想要模仿是不可能的，
因為你會忘記，唯有背下來，説起來才有信心。

3-1 Got a minute?

這句話源自 Have you got a minute? 字面意思是
「你有一分鐘嗎？」引申為「你有空嗎？」(=*Are you
free?*) 也可説成：Do you have a minute? 意思相同。

3-2 You need to hear this.

字面意思是「你需要聽聽這個。」相當於中文的「你
得聽聽這個。」也常説成：This is something you need
to hear. (這件事你得聽聽。) 或 I have something to
tell you. (我有事要告訴你。)

3-3 I have an *interesting* piece of information.

information「消息；資訊」是抽象名詞，不可數，
要用單位名詞表數的觀念，如：

> I have *information* for you. 【正】
> (我有消息要告訴你。)
> *I have an information for you.* 【誤】
> I have *a piece of information* for you. 【正】
> (我有一個消息要告訴你。)
> I have *some information* for you. 【正】
> (我有一些消息要告訴你。)

形容詞應加在單位名詞前：

a *useful* piece of advice　一個有用的勸告

3-4　Pandas are rare animals.

可說成：Pandas are not very common.（貓熊並不常見。）或 Animals like pandas are very rare.（像貓熊這樣的動物很稀少。）

3-5　They are endangered.

danger 是「危險」，endanger 是動詞，指「危害」，endangered 字面意思是「受到危害的」，也就是「瀕臨絕種的」。

3-6　Those *who hunt pandas in China* face the death

penalty *if caught*.

if caught 源自 *if they are caught*。

可說成：Panda hunters in China face the death penalty.（在中國，獵殺貓熊的人會面臨死刑。）（= *Panda hunters in China will face the death penalty.*）還可說成：Panda hunters in China will be put to death.（在中國，獵殺貓熊的人將會被處死。）

在這句話中，face 也可說成 will face。

3-7　Tom **burned the candle** at both ends.

　　　　這句話字面意思是「湯姆一支蠟燭兩頭燒。」引申為「湯姆過分透支體力。」源自諺語：Don't burn the candle at both ends.（不可過分透支體力。）類似的有：Tom stayed up very late.（湯姆熬夜熬到很晚。）Tom worked day and night to finish his project.（湯姆為了完成他的計劃，日夜工作。）

3-8　Then he got sick.

　　　then 在此作「然後；接著」解，是轉承語，連接前面的句子。可說成：Then he got ill.（然後他就生病了。）got 可用 became 代替，說成：Then he became sick. 或 Then he became ill. 意思相同。在此不可說成：*Then he was ill.*（誤）

3-9　*Only **when** you lose your health* will you realize how important it is.

　　　可說成：You will realize how important your health is (*only*) when you lose it.

> Only + 副詞（子句、片語）+ $\left\{ \begin{array}{c} 助 \\ be \end{array} \right\}$ + S + ……

【例】 ***Only by working hard*** can we succeed in doing everything.
= We can **only** succeed in doing everything **by working hard**.
（只有努力工作，我們做每一件事情才能成功。）

UNIT 3　4~6劇情簡介

【提到一位好老師】

4. *He kept his promise.*
   He came despite his illness.
   Not only was he tired but he
   　was also under the weather.

It shows character.
（這顯示出一個人
　的品格。）

He treats us well.
He is more than a teacher.
He is not so much a teacher
　as a friend.

I like him, too.
（我也喜歡他。）

Tom has aged well.
He looks young for his age.
He is not a student but a teacher.

He's very
　handsome.
（他很帥。）

*　*　*

【談論一起去看電影的朋友】

5. *We went to the movies last night.*
   We saw a romantic comedy.
   I enjoyed the movie and so did Tom.

Cool.
（酷。）

He's a great guy.
He's funny and smart.
He earns twice as much as I do.

That's a lot
of money.
(那很多錢。)

He is thrifty.
Spending money is a problem
   for him.
He seldom, if ever, takes a taxi.

Buses are much
cheaper.
(坐公車便宜多了。)

* * *

【談論金錢觀】

6. *Some people are rich, while*
   others are not.
   Some people are happy, while
     others are not.
   Money does not equal happiness.

It doesn't.
(是不等於。)

I don't borrow money, ever.
Instead, I often lend money to
   my friends.
I always seize the chance to
   help others.

That's noble
of you.
(你真是可敬。)

I have not more than 100 dollars.
I have at most 100.
I can lend you what I have.

Thanks a lot.
(非常感謝。)

4. *He is more than a teacher.*

He kept his promise.	他遵守諾言。
He came *despite* his illness. 【和光大】	儘管他生病，他還是來了。
Not only was he tired *but* he was *also* under the weather. 【福岡大】	他不僅很疲倦，而且還身體不舒服。
He treats us well.	他對我們很好。
He is *more than* a teacher.	他不只是老師。
He is *not so much* a teacher *as* a friend. 【早大】	與其說他是個老師，不如說是個朋友。
Tom has *aged well.*	湯姆駐顏有術。
He looks young for his age.	他看起來比實際年齡年輕。
He is *not* a student *but* a teacher. 【文教大】	他不是學生，而是老師喔。

** ————————————————

keep one's promise 遵守諾言

despite〔dɪ'spaɪt〕*prep.* 儘管　　*not only…but also* 不僅…而且

be under the weather 身體不舒服

treat〔trit〕*v.* 對待　　*more than* 不只是

not so much A *as* B 與其說是 A，不如說是 B

age〔edʒ〕*v.* 變老　　*age well* 沒什麼變老；駐顏有術

not A *but* B 不是 A，而是 B

【背景説明】

會説 He is not so much a teacher as a friend. 你的英文會話就更有深度了。如果不背，你不可能 説出這樣好的句子。

4-1 He kept his promise.

可説成：He kept his word. (他遵守諾言。) (= *He was true to his word.*) 和 He was true to his promise. 意思相同。　　word〔wɜd〕*n.* 承諾

keep one's word 遵守諾言　　be true to 忠於

4-2 He came *despite his illness.*

可説成：He came in spite of his illness. (儘管他生 病，他還是來了。) 或 He showed up even though he's sick. (即使他生病，他還是出現了。)

despite〔dɪ'spaɪt〕*prep.* 儘管 (= *in spite of*)

show up 出現　　even though 即使

4-3 *Not only* was he tired, *but* he was *also* under the weather.

> *Not only…but also* (不僅…而且) 是對等連接詞，連接兩個子句，*Not only* 在句首，要倒裝。【詳見「文法寶典」p.467】這句話不可説成：*Not only was he tired, but also he was under the weather.* (誤) 因爲 also 在此是副詞，應放在 be 動詞後。

be under the weather 字面的意思是「在天氣下」，引申為「受到天氣的影響」，再引申為「身體不舒服」。

> *be under the weather* 身體不舒服
> - = be sick
> - = be ill
> - = be unwell

可簡單說成：He was sick and tired. (他又病又疲倦。)
或 In addition to being sick, he was exhausted. (除了生病以外，他筋疲力盡。) 【in addition to　除了…之外 (還有)　exhausted〔ɪgˈzɔstɪd〕*adj.* 筋疲力盡的】

4-4　He treats us *well*.

可說成：He is very nice to us. (他對我們很好。) 或 He takes care of us. (他很照顧我們。) 【take care of　照顧】在這裡用現在式，表示他總是對我們很好。

4-5　He is *more than* a teacher.

more than 在此作「不只是」解，等於 He is not just a teacher. (他不只是一位老師。) (= *There's more to him than just being a teacher.*) 【to 表「屬於；歸於」】

4-6　He is *not so much* a teacher *as* a friend.

> - *not so much* A *as* B　與其說是 A，不如說是 B
> - = *not* A *but* B

可說成：He is more like a friend than a teacher. (他比較像朋友，比較不像老師。) 或 We consider him a friend first, then a teacher. (我們把他當朋友，超過當老師。)【consider〔kən'sɪdə〕*v.* 認為】

4-7 Tom has *aged well*.

age〔edʒ〕*v.* 變老　　*age well* 沒什麼變老；駐顏有術

可說成：Tom still looks young. (湯姆仍然看起來很年輕。) 或 Tom looks good. (湯姆看起來很好。) 或 Tom hasn't aged at all. (湯姆完全沒有變老。)

4-8 He looks young *for his age*.

字面的意思是「以他的年紀而論，他看起來很年輕。」也就是「他看起來比實際年齡年輕。」可說成：He has a youthful appearance. (他看起來很年輕。) 或 Despite his age, he looks very young. (雖然他年紀大，他看起來很年輕。)　　youthful〔'juθfəl〕*adj.* 年輕的　appearance〔ə'pɪrəns〕*n.* 外表

4-9 He is *not* a student *but* a teacher.

not A *but* B 不是A，而是B

可說成：He is a teacher, not a student. (他是老師，不是學生。) 或 He may look like a student, but he's really a teacher. (他可能看起來像學生，但他其實是個老師。)

5. Spending money is a problem for him.

We *went to the movies* last night.	我們昨天晚上去看電影。
We saw *a romantic comedy*.	我們看了一部愛情喜劇片。
I enjoyed the movie and *so did* Tom.【慶應大】	我很喜歡那部電影，而湯姆也是。
He's a great guy.	他是個好人。
He's *funny and smart*.	他既風趣又聰明。
He earns *twice as much as* I do.　【關東學院大】	他賺的錢是我的兩倍。
He is *thrifty*.	他很節省。
Spending money is a problem for him.	他不喜歡花錢。
He *seldom*, *if ever*, takes a taxi.　【京都產業大】	他很少搭計程車。

** ────────────────

go to the movies 去看電影
romantic〔ro'mæntɪk〕adj. 浪漫的；談情說愛的
comedy〔'kɑmədɪ〕n. 喜劇　　enjoy〔ɪn'dʒɔɪ〕v. 喜歡；享受
guy〔gaɪ〕n. 人；傢伙　　funny〔'fʌnɪ〕adj. 好笑的；有趣的
earn〔ɝn〕v. 賺　　thrifty〔'θrɪftɪ〕adj. 節省的
seldom, *if ever* 即使有，也很少；很少

【背景説明】

一旦背完，變成短暫記憶，就要加快速度，變成長期記憶。早上一起床，一面散步，一面背書，效果最好。

5-1 We **went to the movies** last night.

「看電影」的説法很多，從前電影院大多在一起，*go to the movies*「去看電影」中的 movies 是指「電影院」。現在，電影院有時單獨存在，所以也可説成：*go to a movie*。「看電影」也可直接説：*watch a movie* 或 *see a movie*。

下面都是美國人常説的話：

We went to the movies. (我們去看了電影。)
= We went to a movie.
= We saw a movie.
= We watched a movie.
= We went to see a movie.

5-2 We saw **a romantic comedy**.

romantic〔ro'mæntɪk〕*adj.* 浪漫的；談情説愛的
comedy〔'kɑmədɪ〕*n.* 喜劇

常説成：We watched a romantic comedy. (我們看了一部愛情喜劇片。) 或 We saw a sweet and funny movie. (我們看了一部令人愉快而且好笑的電影。)(= *We saw a pleasant and amusing movie.*)
sweet〔swit〕*adj.* 令人愉快的 (= *pleasant*)
funny〔'fʌnɪ〕*adj.* 好笑的 (= *amusing*)

5-3　I enjoyed the movie and *so did* Tom.

　　　　so did Tom 是 so did Tom (*enjoy the movie*) 的省略。
也可説成：Tom and I enjoyed the movie. (湯姆和我都喜
歡這部電影。) 或 We both liked the film. (我們兩個都喜歡
這部影片。)

5-4　He's a great guy.

　　　　可説成：He's a nice guy. (他是個好人。)(= *He's a
good guy.*) guy 單數時通常指男生。這句話還可説成：
He's a great person. 或 He's a great man. 對於女生，
可以説：She's a great lady. (她是個好人。)(= *She's a
great woman.*) person 男女都可以用。

5-5　He's *funny and smart.*

　　　　funny 的意思有「好笑的；滑稽的；有趣的」。可加強
語氣説成：He's so funny and smart. (他非常風趣和聰
明。) 也有人説：He's charming and intelligent. (他有
魅力又聰明。) 或 He's polite and well-mannered. (他
很有禮貌。) 兩個同義的形容詞有加強語氣的作用。

【比較】He's a fun person. (和他在一起很愉快。)
　　　　　(= *He's fun to be with.*)
　　　　　He's a funny person. (他是有趣的人。)
　　　　　(= *He's a humorous person.*)

5-6　He earns *twice as much as I do.*

　　　　倍數 twice 放在 as 的前面。還可説成：He makes
twice as much as I do. (他賺的錢是我的兩倍。) 或 I
make half as much as he does. (我賺的錢是他的一半。)

5-7 He is *thrifty*.

thrifty〔'θrɪftɪ〕*adj.* 節省的

　　常説成：He is frugal.（他很節省。）或 He is tight with his money.（他很吝嗇。）【frugal〔'frugḷ〕*adj.* 節省的 be tight with one's money　吝嗇】

5-8 Spending money is a problem *for him*.

　　這是幽默的話。這句話字面的意思是「花錢對他來說是個問題。」引申為「他不喜歡花錢。」（= *He doesn't like spending money.*）也可説成：He hates to spend money.（他討厭花錢。）【hate〔het〕*v.* 討厭】

　　看到一個人不喜歡早起，就可説：Getting up early is a problem for her.（她不喜歡早起；要她早起很困難。）

5-9 He *seldom, if ever*, takes a taxi.

　　if ever 是插入語，ever = at any time。

seldom, if ever 的意思是「即使有，也很少」，可看成是加強 seldom 的語氣，意思是「我認爲他沒有，有的話也很少」。

　【例】He *seldom, if ever*, smokes.（他很少抽煙。）
　　　　He *seldom, if ever*, drinks.（他很少喝酒。）
　　　　He *seldom, if ever*, comes here.
　　　　（他很少來這裡。）

6. I don't borrow money, ever.

Some people are rich, while **others** are not. 【流通科學大】	有些人有錢,而另一些人沒錢。
Some people are happy, while **others** are not.	有些人快樂,而另一些人不快樂。
Money does not equal happiness.	錢不等於快樂。
I do**n't borrow** money, **ever**.	我絕不會借錢。
Instead, I often **lend** money to my friends. 【芝浦工大】	我反而常借錢給我的朋友。
I always seize the chance to help others.	我總是會抓住機會幫助別人。
I have **not more than** 100 dollars. 【大谷女子大】	我的錢不到一百元。
I have **at most** 100. 【大谷女子大】	我最多只有一百元。
I can lend you what I have.	我可以借你我所有的錢。

**

some…others 有些…另一些　　while〔hwaɪl〕conj. 然而
equal〔'ikwəl〕v. 和…相等;等於　　**not…ever** 從不;絕不
instead〔ɪn'stɛd〕adv. 作爲代替;反而　　seize〔siz〕v. 抓住
not more than 不多於;比…少(= less than)
at most 最多

【背景説明】

一個人背書很無聊，可以找另一個人一起
背，你背一句，我背一句，你背三句，我背三句，
很快就能背下來。

6-1 *Some* people are rich, while *others* are not.
some…others 一些…另一些

可説成：*Some* people have money, while *others*
don't.（有些人有錢，而另一些人沒錢。）或 *Some* people
are poor, and *some* are wealthy.（有些人窮，有些人有
錢。）【wealthy〔ˈwɛlθɪ〕*adj.* 有錢的】

6-2 *Some* people are happy, while *others* are not.

可説成：*Some* people are content, while *others*
are not.（有些人滿足，而另一些人不滿足。）或 *Some*
people enjoy their lives, while *others* don't.（有些人
享受人生，而另一些人沒有。）
【content〔kənˈtɛnt〕*adj.* 滿足的】

6-3 *Money does not equal happiness.*

也常説成：Happiness can't be bought.（快樂不是
能夠買到的。）或 Money can't buy happiness.（錢無法
買到快樂。）

6-4　I do**n't borrow** money, *ever*.

> **not···ever** 相當於 never（從不；絕不），例如：
>
> I do**n't** lie, *ever*.（我從不說謊。）
> I do**n't** steal, *ever*.（我從不偷東西。）
> I wo**n't** love her, *ever*.（我絕不會愛她。）

這句話可加強語氣，說成：I **never** borrow money, *ever*.（我絕不向人借錢。）【never···ever　絕不】

6-5　*Instead*, I *often lend* money to my friends.

> **Instead** 可用 **On the contrary**（相反地）或 **Rather**（而是）來代替。

這句話可說成：**Instead**, my friends borrow money from me all the time.（反而是我朋友總是向我借錢。）【all the time　一直；始終】

lend 是「授與動詞」，如：Lend me some money.（借我一些錢。）間接受詞和直接受詞可對調，成為：Lend some money to me.（借一些錢給我。）

borrow 是及物動詞，可說成：Can I borrow some money?（我可以借一些錢嗎？）

6-6　I *always* seize the chance to help others.

可說成：I always grab the chance to help others.（我總是會抓住機會幫助別人。）或 I never pass up a chance to help others. （我絕不會錯過幫助別人的機會。）

【grab〔græb〕v. 抓住　　pass up 錯過】

6-7 I have *not more than* 100 dollars.

not more than 是「不多於」，就是「少於」（= *less than*）。

可說成：I have less than 100 dollars. （我的錢不到一百元。）或 I have about 100 dollars. （我大約有一百元。）

6-8 I have *at most* 100.

at most 最多

可說成：I have 100 at most. （我最多只有一百元。）或 I probably have less than 100. （我可能少於一百元。）

6-9 I can lend <u>you</u> <u>what I have</u>.
　　　　　　　間受　　　　直受

lend「授與動詞」，有兩個受詞。borrow 是「完全及物動詞」，只有一個受詞。

可說成：You can borrow what I have. （你可以向我借我所有的錢。）可更客氣地說：You're welcome to borrow what I have. （歡迎你向我借我所有的錢。）

UNIT 3 7~9劇情簡介

【重要工作難度高，但不能放棄希望】

7. ***Our task is to finish the work, isn't it?***
   We must finish by 6 p.m.
   Our task is of much importance.

Let's get to work.
（我們開始工作吧。）

It was a tough job.
Nobody could get it done.
To my surprise, you did it.

It wasn't easy.
（真是不容易。）

Never lose hope.
Keep aiming high.
That dream of yours might come true someday.

I won't give up.
（我不會放棄。）

* * *

【不要輕易承諾，有時要找幫手】

8. ***Be genuine.***
   Don't make promises you can't keep.
   Making promises is one thing, keeping them another.

You're right.
（你說的對。）

He's not in.
He's out of town.
I'll have him call you back.

I would
appreciate tha
（謝謝。）

It is a two-person job.
You can't do it alone.
I'll get someone to help you.

Great!
（太好了！）

＊　＊　＊

【談論投票表決的結果】

9. ***They had a heated debate
    at the meeting.***
   I kept silent.
   Some voted for it; others
       voted against it.

That's how it goes.
（事情就是這樣。）

A number of people agreed.
The number of people who
    disagreed was small.
The rest didn't vote.

Interesting.
（有意思。）

You have a lead foot.
Someday you'll have a terrible
    accident.
I hope you slow down.

I will.
（我會的。）

7. *Keep aiming high*.

Our task is to finish the work, *isn't it*? 【上智大】	我們的任務是把工作做完，對不對？
We must finish *by* 6 p.m. 【青山學院大】	我們必須在晚上六點前完成。
Our task is *of* much importance. 【近畿大】	我們的任務很重要。
It was a tough job.	這是個困難的工作。
Nobody could *get it done*.	沒有人能做到。
To my surprise, you did it. 【伸敎大】	想不到你做到了。
Never lose hope.	絕不要失去希望。
Keep *aiming high*.	要持續有遠大的目標。
That dream of yours might *come true* someday. 【駒澤大】	你的夢想有一天可能會實現。

** ────────────────────

task〔tæsk〕*n.* 任務；工作　finish〔'fɪnɪʃ〕*v.* 完成
importance〔ɪm'pɔrtn̩s〕*n.* 重要；重要性
of importance 重要的 (= *important*)
of much importance 非常重要的 (= *very important*)
tough〔tʌf〕*adj.* 困難的　*get it done* 做到
to one's surprise 令某人驚訝的是
aim high 要胸懷大志；要有遠大的目標
come true 實現；成眞
someday〔'sʌm,de〕*adv.* 將來有一天

【背景説明】

　　　　早上起來和晚上睡前，是背書最好的時間。常常
背「一口氣英語」，有助於睡眠，不會胡思亂想。

7-1　Our task is to finish the work, *isn't it*?

　　　　isn't it 是 *isn't it* (*to finish the work*) 的省略。可
說成：Our mission is to complete the work, *isn't it*?
（我們的任務是完成這個工作，對不對？）或 Our goal is
to finish the job, right?（我們的目標是完成這個工作，對
不對？）　　mission〔'mɪʃən〕 *n*. 任務
complete〔kəm'plit〕 *v*. 完成　　goal〔gol〕 *n*. 目標

7-2　We must finish *by* 6 p.m.

　　　　by 作「在…之前」解（= *no later than*）。【詳見「文法
寶典」p.566】這句話也可說成：It must be done by 6 p.m.
（必須在晚上六點前完成。）或 We must have it completed
no later than 6 p.m.（我們必須在晚上六點前完成。）
finish 是及物和不及物兩用動詞。

7-3　Our task is *of* much importance.

of + 抽象名詞 = 形容詞
of much importance 非常重要的（= *very important*）

　　　　可說成：Our task is very important.（我們的任務很
重要。）（= *Our assignment is very important.*）
　　【assignment〔ə'saɪnmənt〕 *n*. 任務】

7-4　It was a tough job.

　　　　可說成：It was a difficult task.（這是個困難的任務。）（= *It was a tough assignment.*）

7-5　Nobody could *get it done*.

　　　　get it done 在這裡的意思是「做到」（= *make it happen* = *do it*）。這句話可說成：Nobody could do it.（沒有人能做到。）（= *Nobody could make it happen.*）

7-6　*To my surprise*, you did it.

　　　　to my surprise 的意思是「令我驚訝的是」，在此作「想不到」解。可說成：*To my amazement*, you did it.（想不到，你做到了。）或 *To my surprise*, you got the job done.（想不到，你做到了。）或 You got it done, much to my surprise.（你做到了，讓我嚇一跳。）
　　【much to one's surprise　令某人非常驚訝的是】

7-7　Never lose hope.

　　　　可說成：Never give up.（永不放棄。）或 Never lose faith.（永不失去信心。）
　　【give up　放棄　　faith〔feθ〕*n.* 信念；信心】

7-8 Keep *aiming high*.

aim high 字面的意思是「向高處瞄準」，引申為「要胸懷大志；要有遠大的目標」。可説成：Reach for the stars. (要設定不易達到的目標。) 【reach for 伸手去拿】

美國人常説下面三句話鼓勵他人：

Dream big dreams. (要有遠大的夢想。)
Reach for the stars. (設定不易達到的目標。)
The sky is your limit. (你的潛力無限大。)
【詳見「一口氣背呼口號英語」p.1】

7-9 That dream *of yours* might *come true* someday.

也可説成：Your dream may come true someday.
(你的夢想總有一天會實現。) 或 It's possible that your dream may come true someday. (可能你的夢想有一天會實現。)

【劉毅老師的話】

「一口氣英語」是語言學習的革命。先學會説正確的英語，就會考試，也會寫文章。傳統的英語學習法，讓大家都不會説，早晚會走入歷史。

8. Be genuine.

Be *genuine*.	要真誠。
Don't *make promises* you can't keep.	不要做你無法實現的承諾。
Making promises is *one thing*, keeping them *another*.	做出承諾是一回事，實現承諾又是另一回事。
【高岡法科大】	
He's not *in*.	他不在。
He's *out of town*.	他出城去了。
I'll *have* him *call* you back.【立命館大】	我會要他回你電話。
It's *a two-person job*.	這是兩個人的工作。
You can't do it alone.	你無法獨自完成。
I'll *get* someone *to help* you.	我會找人來幫你。
【關西學院大】	

**　　————————————

genuine〔ˈdʒɛnjuɪn〕 *adj.* 真的；真誠的
make a promise 做出承諾　　keep〔kip〕*v.* 遵守（承諾）
…is one thing, ~*(is) another* …是一回事，~又是另一回事
be not in 不在　　***be out of town*** 出城
call *sb.* ***back*** 回某人電話　　alone〔əˈlon〕*adv.* 獨自
get〔gɛt〕*v.* 促使…（做~）

【背景説明】

　　　　可利用背「一口氣英語」的機會，訓練自己
的口才，做一個人人都喜歡的人。有時一句好話，
勝過千言萬語。

8-1　Be *genuine*.

　　　　genuine〔'dʒɛnjuɪn〕的主要意思是「眞的」，在此作
「眞誠的；眞心的」解。可説成：Be sincere.（要眞誠。）
或 Be honest.（要誠實。）【sincere〔sɪn'sɪr〕*adj.* 眞誠的】
【genuine 的同義字，詳見「一口氣背同義字寫作文…①」】

8-2　Don't *make promises* you can't keep.

　　　　可説成：Don't exaggerate your ability.（不要誇大
你的能力。）或 Don't promise more than you can
deliver.（不要承諾你做不到的事。）
exaggerate〔ɪg'zædʒə,ret〕*v.* 誇大　　deliver〔dɪ'lɪvɚ〕*v.* 實現

8-3　Making promises is *one thing*, keeping them *another*.

　　　　這句話源自 Making promises *is one thing*, *but*
keeping them *is another*. 省略 but 和 is。可説成：It's
easy to make promises, but difficult to keep them.
（做承諾很容易，但要遵守承諾很難。）或 Keeping a
promise is more difficult than making one.（遵守承諾
比做出承諾困難。）

8-4 He's not in.

　　這句話源自：He's not *in the room*.（他不在這個房間。）He's not *in the office*.（他不在辦公室。）He's not *in the building*.（他不在這棟建築物裡。）等。

　　這句話還可說成：He's not here.（他不在。）
（＝*He's absent.*）【absent〔'æbsn̩t〕*adj.* 缺席的；不在的】

8-5 He's *out of town*.

　　這句話很常用。字面的意思是「他不在城裡。」引申為「他出門了。」可說成：He is away on business.（他出去辦事了。）或 He is not in town.（他不在城裡；他出門了。）【on business 因為公事】

8-6 I'll *have* him *call* you back.

　　have 是「使役動詞」，後接原形動詞，如果改成 get，就要用有 to 的不定詞做受詞補語，說成：I'll *get* him *to call* you back.（我會叫他回你電話。）

　　這句話還可說成：I'll have him return your call.
（我會叫他回你電話。）【return one's call 回某人電話】
或加強語氣說成：I'll make sure he calls you back.
（我會確定他有回你電話。）（＝*I'll see to it that he calls you back.*）

　　【make sure 確定　　see to it that 留意；務必】

8-7 It's *a two-person job*.

　　「數字–單數名詞」是「複合形容詞」，如：a
ten-year-old boy（一個十歲的小男孩）【詳見「文法寶典」
p.87】。這句話也可說成：One person can't handle this
job.（一個人沒辦法處理這個工作。）或 It takes two
people to do this job.（需要兩個人才能做這個工作。）

【handle〔'hændl〕v. 應付；處理　　take〔tek〕v. 需要】

8-8 You can't do it *alone*.

　　這句話相當於 You can't do it by yourself.（你不可
能自己做。）或 You can't handle it on your own.（你無
法自己處理。）

　　可說成：You're going to need help.（你會需要幫
助。）或 It's not possible for one person to do it by
himself.（單獨一個人不可能做。）【by oneself 獨自】

8-9 I'll *get* someone *to help* you.

　　這句話可說成：I'll ask someone to help you.（我
會請他人幫助你。）(= *I'll ask someone to assist you.*)
或 I'll find someone to assist you.（我會找人協助你。）
(= *I'll have someone give you a hand.*)

9. *You have a lead foot*.

They had a heated debate *at the meeting*.【同志社大】	他們在會議上有激烈的辯論。
I kept silent.【同志社大】	我保持沈默。
Some voted for it; *others* voted against it.【四天王寺大】	有些人投贊成票；另一些人投反對票。
A number of people agreed.【九州共立社大】	有許多人同意。
The number of people who disagreed *was* small.【上智大】	不同意的人很少。
The rest didn't vote.【四天王寺大】	其他的人沒有投票。
You *have a lead foot*.【ヤ試】	你開車開得很快。
Someday you'll have a terrible accident.【ヤ試】	有一天你會發生嚴重的車禍。
I hope you *slow down*.	我希望你可以減速。

** ─────────────

heated〔'hitɪd〕*adj.* 激烈的　　debate〔dɪ'bet〕*n.* 辯論；爭論
silent〔'saɪlənt〕*adj.* 沈默的　　vote〔vot〕*v.* 投票
vote for 投票贊成　　*vote against* 投票反對
a number of 一些；許多　　number〔'nʌmbɚ〕*n.* 數目
disagree〔,dɪsə'gri〕*v.* 不同意　　rest〔rɛst〕*n.* 其餘的人或物
lead〔lɛd〕*n.* 鉛　　terrible〔'tɛrəbl̩〕*adj.* 可怕的；嚴重的
slow down 減慢；減速

【背景説明】

　　　背「一口氣英語」急不得，可先聽 CD，了
解整個劇情，再從第一回開始背。第一回背完變
成直覺後，再背其他的就簡單了。

9-1　They had a heated debate *at the meeting*.

heated〔'hitɪd〕 *adj.* 激烈的

debate〔dɪ'bet〕 *n.* 辯論；爭論

　　可説成：They argued at the meeting.（他們在會議
中爭論。）

at the meeting 也可説成 in the meeting。

9-2　I kept silent.

　　　keep 後面可接形容詞做主詞補語。這句話可説成：
I kept my mouth shut.（我都不講話。）(= *I didn't say
anything.*)【shut〔ʃʌt〕 *adj.* 閉上的】

9-3　*Some* voted for it; *others* voted against it.

　　可説成：*Some* were for it; *others* were against it.
（有些人贊成；有些人反對。）或 *Some* supported the
idea; *others* opposed it.（有些人支持這個意見；另一些人
反對。）　　for〔fɔr〕 *prep.* 贊成

against〔ə'gɛnst〕 *prep.* 反對　　oppose〔ə'poz〕 *v.* 反對

9-4　*A **number** of* people agreed.

可說成：A number of people were in agreement.

（有一些人同意。）(= *Some people agreed.*)

【in agreement　同意】

9-5　*The **number** of people **who disagreed was*** small.

核心主詞是 number，動詞用單數 was。可說成：
Few people disagreed.（很少人不同意。）(= *Not many people disagreed.*)

9-6　*The rest* didn't vote.

可說成：The remaining people didn't vote.（剩下的人沒有投票。）(= *The others didn't vote.*)

【remaining〔rɪ'menɪŋ〕*adj.* 剩下的】

9-7　You *have a lead foot*.

lead〔lɛd〕*n.* 鉛

字面的意思是「你有一隻鉛的腳。」因為鉛很重，用重的腳踩油門，引申為「你開車開得太快了。」(= *You drive much too fast.*)

9-8 Someday you'll have a terrible accident.

可說成：You're going to have an accident someday.
（有一天你會出意外。）或 You're headed for trouble if
you continue to drive so fast. （如果你繼續開那麼快，你將
會有麻煩。）【be headed for sth. 很可能即將…】

9-9 I hope you *slow down*.

slow down 減慢；減速

名詞子句做 hope, assume, suppose 的受詞時，可
用現在式代替未來式。

【比較】 I hope you slow down. 【常用】
I hope you will slow down. 【正，少用】
I hope you like it. 【常用】
I hope you will like it. 【少用】

這句話可說成：You'd better slow down. （你最好
減慢速度。）或 You need to slow down. （你需要減慢速
度。）【had better + V. 最好…】

一口氣考試英語 Unit 3

※ 以三組為一個單位較好背。

1. ***What a nice surprise!***
I can't believe my eyes.
Little did I dream of seeing you here. 【駒澤大】

What are you doing ***on*** Sunday? 【帝塚山學院大】
Come stay with us, ***won't you***? 【東海大】
Let's go hiking, ***shall we***? 【東洋大】

You can ride a bike anywhere.
You can rent a bike ***by the hour***. 【姬路獨協大】
There are bicycle paths all around the city.

2. There is a job fair ***on campus*** today.
Many students will be ***attending***.
I'm going ***as well***. 【九州共立大】

Mother held me ***by the*** arm. 【流通經濟大】
She patted me ***on the*** shoulder.
She didn't want me to leave.

I like ***wearing*** black clothing. 【聖學院大】
She prefers to ***dress*** in red. 【聖學院大】
I ***put on*** a vest when it gets cold.

3. Got a minute? (= *Have you got a minute?*)
You need to hear this.
I have ***an interesting piece of*** information. 【中試】

Pandas are rare animals.
They are endangered.
Those who hunt pandas in China face the death penalty ***if caught***. 【慶大】

Tom ***burned the candle at both ends***.
Then he got sick.
Only when you lose your health ***will you*** realize how important it is. 【京都外語大】

* * *

4. ***He kept his promise***.
He came ***despite*** his illness. 【和光大】
Not only was he tired ***but*** he was ***also*** under the weather. 【福岡大】

He treats us well.
He is ***more than*** a teacher.
He is ***not so much*** a teacher ***as*** a friend. 【早大】

Tom has ***aged well***.
He looks young for his age.
He is ***not*** a student ***but*** a teacher. 【文教大】

5. We ***went to the movies*** last night.
We saw ***a romantic comedy***.
I enjoyed the movie and ***so did*** Tom. 【慶應大】

He's a great guy.
He's *funny and smart*.
He earns *twice as much as* I do.
【關東學院大】

He is *thrifty*.
Spending money is a problem for him.
He *seldom*, *if ever*, takes a taxi.
【京都產業大】

6. *Some* people are rich, while *others* are not. 【流通科學大】
Some people are happy, while *others* are not.
Money does not equal happiness.

I do*n't borrow* money, *ever*.
Instead, I often *lend* money to my friends. 【芝浦工大】
I always seize the chance to help others.

I have *not more than* 100 dollars. 【大谷女子大】
I have *at most* 100. 【大谷女子大】
I can lend you what I have.

　　　＊　　＊　　＊

7. *Our task is to finish the work*, *isn't it*? 【上智大】
We must finish *by* 6 pm. 【青山學院大】
Our task is *of* much importance. 【近畿大】

It was a tough job.
Nobody could *get it done*.
To my surprise, you did it. 【佛教大】

※可將這兩頁用手機拍下來背。

Never lose hope.
Keep *aiming high*.
That dream of yours might *come true* someday. 【駒澤大】

8. Be *genuine*.
Don't *make promises* you can't keep.
Making promises is *one thing*, keeping them *another*. 【高岡法科大】

He's not *in*.
He's *out of town*.
I'll *have* him *call* you back. 【立命館大】

It is *a two-person job*.
You can't do it alone.
I'll *get* someone *to help* you. 【關西學院大】

9. They had a heated debate *at the meeting*. 【同志社大】
I kept silent. 【同志社大】
Some voted for it; *others* voted against it. 【四天王寺大】

A number of people agreed. 【九州共立社大】
The number of people who disagreed *was* small. 【上智大】
The rest didn't vote. 【四天王寺大】

You *have a lead foot*. 【ヤ試】
Someday you'll have a terrible accident. 【ヤ試】
I hope you *slow down*.

UNIT 4　1~3劇情簡介

【請朋友不要客氣，鼓勵他專心投入】

1. *Make yourself at home.*
   You can ask anyone for help.
   Everyone here is willing to
      lend you a hand.

Good to know.
（知道這一點很好。）

Our business is growing.
We are starting to make a profit.
But there are still many problems
   to be solved.

We can do it.
（我們可以做到。）

Stay on track.
Don't get distracted.
You will never gain success
   unless you are devoted.

I must stay focused.
（我必須維持專注力。）

* * *

【鼓勵朋友要盡全力】

2. *Do your best to perform your duty.*
   Be an example for others to
      follow.
   Wait for the opportunity to
      get promoted.

Good things come
   to those who wait.
（好事會留給等待的人。）

Seek challenges.
Start your own business.
You can achieve
  independence.

Thanks for the
  encouragement.
(謝謝你的鼓勵。)

What makes for a happy life?
To do what we love is not
  enough.
We must like the things we
  have to do.

It's not an
  easy task.
(這不是件容易的事。)

* * *

【邀請朋友一起運動】

3. *I always go jogging in the*
   morning.
   I usually do push-ups as well.
   My goal is to stay in shape.

You're looking
  good.
(你看起來好極了。)

It's quite hot today.
The weekend is approaching.
Do you feel like going for a swim?

Yes, I'd love to.
(好啊，我很樂意。)

Do you play badminton?
It's my favorite sport.
Would you like to play sometime?

Sure, let me
  know when.
(當然好，什麼時候
  通知我。)

1. Make yourself at home.

Make yourself *at home*.	請不要客氣。
You can *ask* anyone *for* help.	你可以請任何人幫忙。
【2014 安徽】	
Everyone here is willing to *lend you a hand*. 【2014 安徽】	這裡的每一個人都願意幫助你。
Our business is *growing*.	我們的事業正在成長。
We are starting to *make a profit*.	我們就要開始獲利。
But there are still many problems *to be solved*. 【2014 北京】	但是仍然有很多問題需要解決。
Stay on track.	做正確的事。
Don't *get distracted*.	不要分心。
You will never gain success unless you *are devoted*.	除非你全心投入，否則你不會獲得成功。
【2014 湖南】	

** ————————————

at home 在家；輕鬆自在的　　willing〔'wɪlɪŋ〕*adj.* 願意的
lend sb. a hand 幫助某人　　profit〔'prɑfɪt〕*n.* 利潤
make a profit 獲利　　solve〔salv〕*v.* 解決
track〔træk〕*n.* 軌道　　distract〔dɪ'strækt〕*v.* 使分心
gain〔gen〕*v.* 獲得　　devoted〔dɪ'votɪd〕*adj.* 專心的

【背景説明】

當一個新進人員到你的公司上班,你就可以
説這九句話。

1-1 Make yourself *at home*.

這句話字面的意思是「使你自己像在家一樣。」引申
爲「請不要客氣。」或「請不要拘束。」美國人也常説:
My home is your home. (= *My place is your place*.)
(我的家就是你家。)

1-2 You can *ask* anyone *for* help.

ask sb. for sth. 請求某人某事

這句話也可説成 : Feel free to ask anyone for
help. (不用客氣,可以請任何人幫忙。)

1-3 Everyone *here* is willing to *lend you a hand*.

lend sb. a hand 幫助某人 (= *give sb. a hand* = *help sb.*)

也可説成 : All those *here* are willing to help you.
(這裡所有的人都願意幫助你。)

1-4　Our business is ***growing***.

　　　　grow 一般作「生長」解，這裡是指「成長」。這句話也可說成：Our business is expanding.（我們的事業正在擴張。）或 Our business is improving.（我們的事業越來越好。）

1-5　We are starting to ***make a profit***.

　　　　用「現在進行式」可表示「不久的將來」。這句話也可說成：We are beginning to make a profit.（我們就要開始獲利。）或 We are starting to make money.（我們就要開始賺錢。）

1-6　But there are ***still many*** problems ***to be solved***.

　　　　But 是轉承語，連接前面的句子。這句話也可說成：We still have difficult tasks to overcome.（我們仍然有困難的任務要克服。）

1-7　***Stay on track.***

　　　　這句話字面的意思是「待在軌道上。」引申為「做正確的事。」等於 Stay focused on your goal.（專注於你的目標。）或 Don't go astray.（不要誤入歧途。）

focused〔'fokəst〕*adj.* 專注的 < *on* >
astray〔ə'stre〕*adv.* 迷路地；走入歧途地
go astray　誤入歧途

1-8 Don't *get distracted*.

　　distract 的意思是「使分心」，這句話的意思是「不要
分心。」也就是 Don't take your eyes off the goal.（不
要偏離目標。）也可說成：Pay attention to what you
have to do.（專心做你該做的事。）

1-9 You will *never* gain success *unless you are devoted*.

be devoted 專心；投入（= *devote oneself*）

　　unless 引導表「條件」的副詞子句，等於 if…not，
修飾 gain，這句話等於：You will never gain success
if you are not devoted.（如果你不全心投入，你就不會獲
得成功。）也可說成：You won't succeed without
dedication.（不專心不會成功。）
【dedication〔͵dɛdə'keʃən〕*n.* 獻身；致力】

　　2014 年湖南的題目是：You will never gain
success unless you are fully devoted to your work.
（除非你全心投入你的工作，否則你不會獲得成功。）我
們把它縮短，為了讓同學好背。

2. Seek challenges.

Do your best to *perform* your *duty*.　【2014 安徽】	盡力做好你的職責。
Be an *example* for others to *follow*.	做一個讓別人效法的榜樣。
Wait for the opportunity to *get promoted*.【2014 安徽】	等待升遷的機會。
Seek challenges.	尋求挑戰。
Start your own business.	要自行創業。
You can *achieve independence*.　【2014 江西】	你可以獲得獨立。
What *makes for* a happy life?　【2014 湖南】	什麼有助於快樂的生活？
To do what we love is not enough.　【2014 湖南】	做我們愛做的事是不夠的。
We must like the things we have to do.【2014 湖南】	我們必須喜歡我們要做的事。

** ———————————————

perform〔pə'fɔrm〕*v.* 執行；做

duty〔'djutɪ〕*n.* 責任；義務；職責

example〔ɪg'zæmpḷ〕*n.* 榜樣　　follow〔'falo〕*v.* 效法

promote〔pro'mot〕*v.* 晉升　　seek〔sik〕*v.* 尋求

challenge〔'tʃælɪndʒ〕*n.* 挑戰

achieve〔ə'tʃiv〕*v.* 獲得　　*make for* 有助於

【背景説明】

　　　下面九句都是激勵別人的話，常常鼓勵別
人，自己受益最大。

2-1　Do your best *to perform your duty*.

　　　這句話的意思是「盡力做好你的職責。」(= *Do your best to do your duty.*) 也可說成：Do your best to fulfill your duty. (盡力完成你的職責。)

2-2　Be an *example for others to follow*.

　　　這句話的意思是「做一個讓別人效法的榜樣。」也可說成：Be a role model for others to follow. 「做一個別人可以效法的模範。」

【role model　模範】

2-3　Wait for the opportunity *to get promoted*.

　　　這句話的意思是「等待晉升的機會。」也可說成：Be patient for the chance to advance. (要耐心等待晉升的機會。)

patient〔ˈpeʃənt〕*adj.* 有耐心的

advance〔ədˈvæns〕*v.* 前進；晉升

2-4 *Seek challenges*.

　　這句話的意思是「尋求挑戰。」可加長為：Seek
challenges to improve yourself. (尋找挑戰來改進自
己。) 美國人也常説：Look for tough jobs. (尋找困
難的工作。)

【tough〔tʌf〕*adj.* 困難的】

2-5 *Start* your own business.

　　這句話字面的意思是「開始你自己的事業。」引申為
「要自行創業。」(= *Do your own thing.* = *Be your own
boss.*)

2-6 You can *achieve independence*.

　　這句話字面的意思是「你可以獲得獨立。」也可説
成：You can achieve freedom. (你可以獲得自由。) 或
You get to call the shots. (你可以發號施令。)

【get to V. 得以~　　call the shots 發號施令】

2-7 What *makes for* a happy life?

　　make for 主要意思有：①前往 ②有助於，在此當
「有助於」解。也可説成：What makes people happy?
(什麼能使人快樂？) 或 What determines a happy
life? (什麼能決定快樂的生活？)

【determine〔dɪˈtɜmɪn〕*v.* 決定】

2-8 <u>To do what we love</u> is not enough.
名　詞　子　句

　　　這句話的意思是「做我們愛做的事是不夠的。」

(= *To do what we love is not sufficient.*)

【sufficient〔sə'fɪʃənt〕*adj.* 足夠的】

2-9 We must like the things *we have to do.*

　　　這句話的意思是「我們必須喜歡我們要做的事。」

(= *We must enjoy our daily job.*)

【daily〔'delɪ〕*adj.* 每天的；日常的】

美國人常說：

　　　Do what we love. (做我們愛做的事。)

　　　Love what we do. (愛我們做的事。)

　　　Big money will follow us. (大錢會跟著來。)

　　　現在我們又學到了更進一步的人生觀，出題教授
太厲害了。

　　　What makes for a happy life?

　　　To do what we love is not enough.

　　　We must like the things we have to do.

在人生當中，有很多事你必須做，不喜歡也得喜歡，
否則你會因壓力而生病。

3. *Do you play badminton?*

I always *go jogging* in the morning.【2014 江蘇】	我早上一定會去慢跑。
I usually *do push-ups* as well.【2014 江蘇】	我通常也做伏地挺身。
My goal is to *stay in shape*.【2014 江蘇】	我的目標是保持健康。
It's *quite hot* today.【2014 陝西】	今天天氣很熱。
The weekend is approaching.	週末快要到了。
Do you *feel like* going for a swim?【2014 陝西】	你想要去游泳嗎？
Do you *play badminton*?【2014 安徽】	你打不打羽毛球？
It's my favorite sport.	它是我最喜愛的運動。
Would you like to play sometime?	你要不要找時間去打？

**　** ————————————

jog〔dʒɑg〕v. 慢跑　　push-up〔'puʃ͵ʌp〕n. 伏地挺身
as well 也（= *too*）　　*stay in shape* 保持健康
approach〔ə'protʃ〕v. 接近　　swim〔swɪm〕n. 游泳
go for a swim 去游泳（= *go swimming*）
badminton〔'bædmɪntən〕n. 羽毛球
sometime〔'sʌm͵taɪm〕adv. 某時

【背景説明】

下面九句話你天天都可以用得到，你可以用
來邀請朋友和你一起運動。

3-1 I *always **go jogging** in the morning*.

這句話的意思是「我早上一定會去慢跑。」always 可
作「總是；老是；一定」解。go jogging 是「去慢跑」。這
句話也可説成：I always go for a jog in the morning.
意思相同。

---

go jogging　去慢跑	go swimming　去游泳
= go for a jog	= go for a swim

不能説成：I always run slowly in the morning.「我早
上總是跑得很慢。」因爲暗示「我早上精神都不太好。」
(= *I'm not a morning person.*)

3-2 I *usually **do push-ups** as well*.

這句話的意思是「我通常也會做伏地挺身。」
push-up 字面的意思是「推又上來」，
「推地面，身體往上」，即「伏地挺身」。

sit-up 字面意思是「(躺下後) 坐起
來」，即「仰臥起坐」。

as well 也 (= *too*)

push-up

sit-up

3-3　My goal is to *stay in shape*.

下面是「我的目標是保持健康。」的各種說法：

My goal is to
- *stay in shape*.
- stay healthy.
- keep in shape.
- keep healthy.
- be fit.
- maintain good health.

3-4　It's *quite hot* today.

這句話的意思是「今天天氣很熱。」也可說成：
What a hot day! (天氣好熱！) 或 The temperature is
very high today. (今天溫度很高。)

3-5　The weekend is approaching.

approach 是「接近」，這句話字面意思是「週末正
在接近。」，引申為「週末快要到了。」(= *The weekend
is coming.*) 也可說成：The weekend is almost here.
或 The weekend is on its way.，意思相同。

3-6　Do you *feel like* going for a swim?

這句話的意思是「你想要去游泳嗎？」也可說成：
Do you feel like going swimming? 或 Do you want
to go swimming? 意思相同。
feel like + V-ing 表「想要～」。

3-7 Do you *play badminton*?

這句話的意思是「你打不打羽毛球？」也可說成：Do you like to play badminton?（你喜不喜歡打羽毛球？）

【注意】 play + 運動名稱，不加冠詞。
如：play basketball（打籃球）、play tennis（打網球）等。

3-8 It's my favorite sport.

這句話的意思是「它是我最喜愛的運動。」(= *It's the sport I like best.* = *It's my favorite physical activity.*)

3-9 *Would you like* to play *sometime*?

這句話的意思是「你要不要找時間去打？」(= *Would you like to play with me sometime?*)

Would you like 和 *Do you like* 不同：
Would you like 是「你要不要」(= *Do you want*)。如果有個外國人到你家，你想問他喜不喜歡吃巧克力，說成：Would you like some chocolate? 他要吃的話，會說："Yes, please." 如果你沒有巧克力不是很尷尬？所以，*Do you like* 是「你喜不喜歡」，*Would you like* 是「你要不要」。
sometime 某個時候 *some time* 一些時間
如：We have been waiting for *some time*.
（我們已經等了一段時間了。）

UNIT 4　4~6劇情簡介

【聊到一位失業的朋友】

4. ***I have been trying to phone Tom.***
There must be something
　wrong with the network.
I can't seem to get through.

Try again later.
（待會再試試看。）

Tom is away from home
　quite a bit.
He seldom sees his family.
He misses his children.

It must be
hard on him.
（他一定很不好受。）

He is thought to have acted
　foolishly.
Now, he is out of a job.
He has no one to blame but
　himself.

I feel bad for him.
（我替他感到難過。）

* * *

【介紹自己的家鄉】

5. ***This is the village where I
was born.***
Now it has grown into a town.
In addition to the school, the
　village has a clinic.

It's a nice
place.
（這裡是個
好地方。）

The forest park is far away.
It is not easy to get to.
The road to get there is
    dangerous.

Let's stay here
    instead.
(那我們改留在這裡。)

I can't meet you on Sunday.
I'll be otherwise occupied.
Maybe next time we can meet.

OK. (好的。)

* * *

【邀請別人野餐】

6. *I'll check my schedule.*
    Call me tomorrow.
    I'll let you know when I am free.

Please do.
(請這麼做。)

I've prepared all kinds of food
    for the picnic.
There's no need to bring
    anything.
We'll have a wonderful time.

I can't wait!
(我等不及了!)

Excuse me.
I'd like your attention.
Please look up from your
    cell phone.

What do you want?
(你想要什麼?)

4. *I can't seem to get through*.

I *have been trying* to phone Tom. 【2014 湖北】	我一直想打電話給湯姆。
There *must be* something wrong with the network. 【2014 湖北】	線路一定有問題。
I can't seem to *get through*. 【2014 湖北】	我似乎無法打通。
Tom is away from home *quite a bit*. 【2014 全國大綱】	湯姆常常不在家。
He *seldom* secs his family. 【2014 全國大綱】	他很少看到他的家人。
He misses his children.	他想念他的小孩。
He is thought *to have acted* foolishly. 【2014 江西】	大家都認為他做了蠢事。
Now, he is out of a job.	現在，他失業了。
He has *no* one to blame *but himself*. 【2014 江西】	他只能怪他自己。

**

phone〔fon〕*v.* 打電話給
network〔'nɛt,wɝk〕*n.* 網路；線路
get through 打通（電話）　　*quite a bit* 常常
act〔ækt〕*v.* 做事；行動　　foolishly〔'fulɪʃlɪ〕*adv.* 愚蠢地
out of a job 失業的　　blame〔blem〕*v.* 責備
but〔bʌt〕*prep.* 除了（= *except*）

【背景説明】

和外國人在一起，剛開始喜歡談天氣，熟
了之後，就開始談論他人。

4-1 *I have been trying* to phone Tom.

「現在完成進行式」表示「從過去到現在持續的
動作」，可說是「現在完成式」的加強語氣。

這句話的意思是「我一直想打電話給湯姆。」

$$I\ have\ been\ trying\ to \begin{cases} \text{call【第一常用】} \\ \text{phone【第四常用】} \\ \text{contact【第三常用】} \\ \text{get in touch with} \\ \qquad\text{【第二常用】} \\ \text{talk with【第五常用】} \end{cases} Tom.$$

4-2 There *must be* something wrong with the network.

「must + 原形動詞」表「對現在或未來的推測」。
There is something wrong with～ 表「～有問題」。

這句話的意思是「線路一定有問題。」(= *There
must be a problem with the connection.*)

network 是「網路」，包含電話線路 (phone
network)、電腦網路 (computer network) 等。

4-3　I can't seem to *get through.*

　　　　這句話的意思是「我似乎無法打通。」*get through* 是指「打通（電話）」。可加長爲：I can't seem to get through to him.（我似乎無法打通電話給他。）(= *I can't seem to reach him.*)

> *I can't seem to* 是很好的句型，例如：
>
> *I can't seem to* ⎧ find him.（我似乎無法找到他。）
> 　　　　　　　⎨ get in touch with him.
> 　　　　　　　⎪ （我似乎無法連絡到他。）
> 　　　　　　　⎩ contact him.（我似乎無法連絡到他。）

4-4　Tom is away from home *quite a bit.*

　　　　這句話的意思是「湯姆常常不在家。」也可說成：Tom is not home quite a bit.（湯姆常常不在家。）

> *quite a bit*（常常）源自 quite a bit of time，等於 quite often。
>
> 　　not home 和 not at home 不同，not at home 是「暫時不在家」。

4-5　He *seldom* sees his family.

　　　　這句話的意思是「他很少看到他的家人。」(= *He doesn't see his family often.*) family 可作「家庭」和「家人」解。

4-6 He misses his children.

　　　　這句話的意思是「他想念他的小孩。」(= *He thinks about his kids a lot.*)

4-7 He is thought *to have acted* foolishly.

> 　　　　「完成式的不定詞」表示「比主要動詞先發生」。這句話的意思是「大家都認為他做了蠢事。」主動的形式是：People think he acted foolishly. (= *People think his actions unwise.*)

4-8 Now, he is out of a job.

　　　　這句話的意思是「現在，他失業了。」Now 後有無逗點皆可，可加強語氣說成 Right now (現在) 而 *out of a job* (失業) 等於 out of work 或 jobless。

4-9 He has *no* one to blame *but himself*.

　　　　這句話的字面意思是「他沒有人可以責備，除了他自己。」引申為「他只能怪他自己。」(= *He has only himself to blame.*)

but 的前面有否定字，but 可作「除了」解 (= *except*)。

5. I'll be otherwise occupied.

This is the village *where* I was born.【2014 陝西】	這是我出生的村莊。
Now it has *grown into* a town.【2014 陝西】	現在它已經變成城鎮了。
In addition to the school, the village has a clinic.【2014 陝西】	除了學校以外，這個村莊還有診所。
The forest park is *far away*.【2014 北京】	這座森林公園很遠。
It is not easy to *get to*.	不容易到達。
The road to *get there* is dangerous.	到那裡的路很危險。
I can't meet you on Sunday.【2014 江蘇】	我禮拜天無法見你。
I'll be *otherwise* occupied.【2014 江蘇】	我有其他的事要忙。
Maybe next time we can meet.	也許下次我們可以見面。

** ——————————

village〔'vɪlɪdʒ〕*n.* 村莊　　*grow into* 變成（ = *become*）
in addition to 除了…之外（還有）
clinic〔'klɪnɪk〕*n.* 診所　　*get to* 到達
otherwise〔'ʌðɚ,waɪz〕*adv.* 否則；在其他方面
occupied〔'ɑkjə,paɪd〕*adj.* 忙碌的

【背景説明】

說話是種藝術，先說 *I can't meet you on Sunday*. 會讓別人覺得不舒服，如果再加上兩句：*I'll be otherwise occupied. Maybe next time we can meet.* 誠意就夠了。

5-1 This is the village *where I was born.*

這句話的意思是「這是我出生的村莊。」美國人也常說：This is my birthplace. (這是我的出生地。) This little town is my place of birth. (這個小鎮是我出生的地方。) 或 This is my hometown. (這是我的家鄉。)

【birthplace ('bɜθ,ples) *n.* 出生地
hometown ('hom'taʊn) *n.* 家鄉】

5-2 Now it has *grown into* a town.

這句話的意思是「現在它已經變成城鎮了。」(= *Now it has become a town.* = *Now it has developed into a town.*)

5-3 *In addition to the school*, the village has a clinic.

clinic ('klınık) *n.* 診所 (= *a small hospital*)

這句話的意思是「除了學校以外，這個村莊還有診所。」

in addition to 和 except 都作「除了～之外」解，但句意完全不同，in addition to 是「除了～之外（再加上）」，except 是「除了～之外（不包括）」。【詳見「文法寶典」p.570】

in addition to 除了…之外（還有）
$\begin{cases} = \text{besides} \\ = \text{aside from} \end{cases}$
$\begin{cases} = \text{apart from} \\ = \text{other than} \end{cases}$

5-4　The forest park is *far away*.

　　　這句話的意思是「這座森林公園很遠。」也可說成：This forest park is a remote place.（這座森林公園在很遠的地方。）或 This forest park is not near the city.（這座森林公園離城市不近。）

【remote〔rɪˈmot〕*adj.* 遙遠的】

5-5　It is not easy *to **get to***.

　　　這句話的意思是「不容易到達。」（= *It is not easy to reach.* = *It is not easy to travel to.*）【travel to 前往】

5-6　The road *to **get there*** is dangerous.

　　　這句話的意思是「到那裡的路很危險。」（= *The way to there is dangerous.*）也可說成：The road *to get there* is not safe.（到那裡的路不安全。）

5-7 I can't meet you *on Sunday*.

　　這句話可以更禮貌地說成：Sorry, I can't meet you on Sunday. (抱歉，我禮拜天無法見你。) (= *Sorry, I can't make it on Sunday.*)

【make it 成功；辦到；能來】

5-8 I'll be *otherwise* occupied.

otherwise〔'ʌðə‚waɪz〕*adv.* ①否則②在其他方面

　　這句話的意思是「我還有其他的事要忙。」(= *I'll be busy with other things.*) 也可說成：I have something else to do. (我有其他的事要做。) 加上 *otherwise* 是比較有禮貌的說法，只說 I'll be occupied. 較不禮貌。

5-9 *Maybe next time* we can meet.

　　這句話的意思是「也許下一次我們可以見面。」美國人也常說：*Hopefully* next time we can meet. (希望我們下次能夠見面。) 或 How about we meet next time? (我們下次見面如何？) 還可說成：Maybe we can meet some other time. (也許我們可以改天見面。)

6. *I'll check my schedule*.

I'll check my schedule.	我要查看我的時間表。
Call me tomorrow.【2014 全國大綱】	明天打電話給我。
I'll let you know *when I am free*.【2014 全國大綱】	我會告訴你我何時有空。
I've *prepared* all kinds of food *for* the picnic.【2014 湖南】	我已經準備好野餐的各種食物。
There is no need to bring anything.	不需要帶任何東西。
We'll have a wonderful time.	我們會玩得很愉快。
Excuse me.	對不起。
I'd like your attention.	請注意聽我說。
Please *look up from* your cell phone.【2014 安徽】	請抬頭不要看手機。

** ——————————————

check〔tʃɛk〕*v.* 檢查；查看
schedule〔'skɛdʒul〕*n.* 時間表
free〔fri〕*adj.* 有空的　　prepare〔prɪ'pɛr〕*v.* 準備
attention〔ə'tɛnʃən〕*n.* 注意
look up 往上看　　*cell phone* 手機

【背景説明】

別人要邀請你時，你可以先説：I'll check my schedule. 不要馬上拒絶，這是一種説話的藝術，儘可能不要直接説 "No."。

6-1 I'll check my schedule.

這句話的意思是「我要查看我的時間表。」也可説成：I'll see if I'm available. (我要看看我有沒有空。)【available〔ə'veləbḷ〕adj. 有空的】或 I'll look and see if I have time. (我要看一看我有沒有時間。) look and see 和中國人的思想「看一看」不謀而合。

6-2 Call me tomorrow.【第一常用】
= Phone me tomorrow.【第二常用】
= Give me a ring tomorrow.【第三常用】
= Give me a buzz tomorrow.【第四常用】

這四個句子的意思都是「明天打電話給我。」命令句只有一種時態，不管現在或未來，都用現在式。
phone〔fon〕v. 打電話給
give sb. a ring 打電話給某人 (= give sb. a buzz)

6-3 I'll let you know *when I am free*.
名詞子句

這句話有兩個意思：
①我會告訴你我何時有空。【when 引導名詞子句】
②當我有空的時候，我會告訴你。【when 引導副詞子句】

在這裡，第一個意思較合理。原則上，名詞子句表「未來」要用「未來式」，這裡是例外。像 Are you free tomorrow? 較少說成：Will you be free tomorrow? 如果這句話改成：I'll let you know when I'll be free. 它只有一個意思：「我會告訴你我何時有空。」

6-4 I've *prepared* all kinds of food *for* the picnic.

這句話的意思是「我已經準備好野餐的各種食物。」all kinds of food（各種食物）也可說成 all types of food（各種食物）或 many different foods（很多不同的食物）。

6-5 *There is no need to* bring anything.

這句話的意思是「不需要帶任何東西。」可以縮短爲：No need to bring anything.（不需要帶任何東西。）也可以加長爲：There is no need for you to bring anything.（你不需要帶任何東西。）

6-6 We'll have a wonderful time.

這句話的意思是「我們會玩得很愉快。」(= *We'll have a great time.*)

6-7 Excuse me.

要引起別人注意時，常說 Excuse me.（對不起。）現在美國人更常說：'Scuse me. 字典上查不到，'Scuse 唸成〔skjuz〕。

這句話也可說成：Pardon me.（對不起。）或 Hey, sorry to interrupt.（嘿，對不起打擾了。）或 Pardon me for interrupting.（抱歉，打擾了。）

【interrupt〔͵ɪntə'rʌpt〕 *v.* 打斷】

6-8 *I'd like your attention.*

在機場我們常聽到：May I have your attention, please?（請大家注意。）*I'd like your attention.* 的意思是「**請你注意聽我說。**」(= *Please listen to me.*) 也可說成：Please give me your attention.（請注意。）

6-9 Please *look up from* your cell phone.

現代人常低頭玩手機，很多人頸椎都出毛病。這句話的意思是「請抬頭不要看手機。」也可說成：Stop looking at your cell phone.（停止看手機。）或加強語氣說成：Get your nose out of that cell phone. （不要看手機。）句中的 nose 可改成 head，意思相同。

UNIT 4　7~9劇情簡介

【和朋友聊書、聊上課】

7. ***The book was published 30
　　years ago.***
It is still popular.
It has stood the test of time.

I should read it.
（我應該讀一讀。）

Every class is exciting.
First, a lecture is given.
Then, a lively question-
and-answer session follows.

You must love
your teacher.
（你一定很愛
你的老師。）

I like lying on the grass.
I enjoy staring at the night
　sky.
There is no greater pleasure
　than being outdoors.

I feel the
same way.
（我有同樣的感覺。）

* * *

【提到掉東西、身上沒錢】

8. ***Dear me!***
Somebody has left the
　door open.
Something could have
　been stolen.

Luckily, everything
is still here.
（幸好，所有東西都還在。）

My key went missing.
My friend helped me find it.
I gave him a nice reward.

You're very kind.
（你人真好。）

Having spent all your money,
    you couldn't afford to eat.
I was broke, too.
Otherwise, I would have helped you.

I know.
（我知道。）

* * *

【問候朋友、勸人少吃】

9. *How was your day?*
What was the highlight?
Anything interesting?

I had a wonderful
    walk in the park.
（我在公園散步非常愉快。）

Once you start eating less,
    your weight will drop.
Keeping it off is difficult.
You must stick it out.

This is true.
（非常正確。）

You have helped me greatly.
You've assisted me in many
    ways.
I'm indebted to you.

I am happy to help.
（我很樂意幫忙。）

7. *It has stood the test of time.*

The book was published 30 years ago.	這本書是三十年前出版的。
It is still popular. 【2014 安徽】	它仍然受人歡迎。
It has *stood the test of time*. 【2014 安徽】	它經得起時間的考驗。
Every class is exciting.	每一堂課都令人興奮。
First, a lecture is given. 【2014 江蘇】	首先先講課。
Then, a lively *question-and-answer session* follows. 【2014 江蘇】	然後，接下來就是熱烈的問與答時間。
I like *lying on the grass*. 【2014 湖南】	我喜歡躺在草地上。
I enjoy *staring at* the night sky. 【2014 湖南】	我喜歡凝視著夜空。
There is *no greater* pleasure *than* being outdoors. 【2014 湖南】	沒什麼比待在戶外更快樂了。

** ——————

publish〔'pʌblɪʃ〕*v.* 出版　　stand〔stænd〕*v.* 忍受
stand the test of time 經得起時間的考驗
lecture〔'lɛktʃɚ〕*n.* 講課；演講
lively〔'laɪvlɪ〕*adj.* 熱烈的　　session〔'sɛʃən〕*n.* 一段時間
a question-and-answer session 問與答時間
follow〔'falo〕*v.* 緊跟在後；隨之而來
grass〔græs〕*n.* 草地　　stare〔stɛr〕*v.* 凝視 <at>

【背景説明】

這一回九句，談到書本、談到上課，和在戶外的樂趣。

7-1 The book was published *30 years ago*.

這句話的意思是「這本書三十年前出版。」也可説成：The book has been in print for 30 years. (這本書已經出版三十年。)【in print 已出版的】

7-2 It is *still* popular.

這句話的意思是「它仍然受人歡迎。」(= *People still enjoy it.*) 也可説成：It still sells well. (它仍然暢銷。)【sell〔sɛl〕v. (東西) 賣出去】

7-3 It has *stood the test of time*.
stand the test of time 經得起時間的考驗

這句話的意思是「它經得起時間的考驗。」也可説成：It has endured the test of time. 或 It has withstood the test of time. 意思相同。

endure〔ɪn'djur〕v. 忍受　　withstand〔wɪθ'stænd〕v. 忍受

7-4 Every class is exciting.

學生常説：「老師教得很好。每一堂課都精彩。」Every class is exciting. (每一堂課都令人興奮。) 也有

人説：Each class is interesting.（每一堂課都有趣。）
或 All classes are great.（每一堂課都很棒。）

7-5　*First*, a lecture is given.

lecture〔'lɛktʃɚ〕*n.* 講課；演講

　　這句話的意思是「首先先講課。」也可説成：In
the beginning, there is a lecture.（起初是講課。）

7-6　*Then*, a lively *question-and-answer session* follows.

lively〔'laɪvlɪ〕*adj.* 熱烈的
session〔'sɛʃən〕*n.* 一段時間（= *a period of time used*
　for a particular activity）
question-and-answer session　問答時間
follow〔'falo〕*v.* 緊跟在後；隨之而來

　　這句話的意思是「然後，接下來就是熱烈的問與答
時間。」也可説成：After that, a spirited Q and A
session follows. 或 After that, there is an active
discussion. 意思相同。

spirited〔'spɪrɪtɪd〕*adj.* 有精神的；活潑的
active〔'æktɪv〕*adj.* 活潑的；熱情的

　　很多人不清楚 session 的用法，在這裡指「一段
時間」，如 a training session（訓練時間）、a photo
session（拍照時間）、a recording session（錄音時間），
此時的 session 不可用 *time* 代替。

7-7 I like *lying on the grass*.

> grass 是「草；草地」,「在草地上」是 *on the grass*
> 或 *in the grass*,不要錯把 *grassland* 當成「草地」,
> *grassland* 指「草原；大片草地；牧場」(= *a large area*
> *of land where wild grass grows*)。
>
> I like lying on the grass. 是「我喜歡躺在草地
> 上。」,「我喜歡坐在草地上。」是 I like sitting on the
> grass。這句話可說成:I like to lie on the grass. 或
> I enjoy lying on the grass.,句中的 on 都可改成 in。

7-8 I enjoy *staring at* the night sky.

> 這句話的意思是「我喜歡凝視著夜空。」(= *I really*
> *like to gaze up at the night sky.*)【gaze〔gez〕*v.* 凝視】

7-9 There is *no greater* pleasure *than being outdoors*.
outdoors〔'aut,dorz〕*adv.* 在戶外

> 這句話的意思是「沒有什麼比待在戶外更快樂了。」
> 也可說成:Being out in Mother Nature is my
> greatest enjoyment.(待在戶外大自然是我最大的享受。)
> 或 I love the great outdoors best!(我最喜歡戶外了!)
> 【Mother Nature 大自然】

8. Dear me!

Dear me! 【2014 江蘇】	天啊！
Somebody has *left the door open*. 【2014 江蘇】	有人門沒關。
Something *could have been* stolen.	可能會有東西被偷。
My key *went missing*. 【2014 全國大綱】	我的鑰匙不見了。
My friend helped me find it.	我的朋友幫我找到它。
I gave him a nice *reward*.	我給他一個很好的報酬。
Having spent all your money, you couldn't *afford to* eat. 【2014 江西】	因爲花光所有的錢，所以你沒錢吃飯。
I was *broke*, too.	我也沒錢。
Otherwise, I would have helped you.	否則我就會幫你。

** ─────────────

Dear me! 天啊！（ = *My God!*）
leave〔liv〕*v.* 使處於（某種狀態）
go missing 不見了（ = *be lost*）
reward〔rɪ'wɔrd〕*n.* 報酬；獎賞
afford〔ə'fɔrd〕*v.* 負擔得起　　broke〔brok〕*adj.* 沒錢的
otherwise〔'ʌðə,waɪz〕*adv.* 否則

【背景說明】

一般人只會用 "My God!"，你會說 "Dear me!"、"My Goodness!" 等。下面九句話常常都可以用得到。

8-1 ***Dear me!***

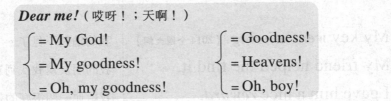

Dear me! (哎呀！；天啊！)
- = My God!
- = My goodness!
- = Oh, my goodness!
- = Goodness!
- = Heavens!
- = Oh, boy!

8-2 Somebody has ***left the door open***.

leave〔liv〕v. 使處於（某種狀態）

這句話的意思是「有人門沒關。」(= *Somebody has left the door unlocked.*)【unlocked〔ʌn'lɑkt〕*adj.* 沒鎖的】也可說成：Somebody did not close the door. (有人沒關門。)

句中的 Somebody 可用 Someone 來代替。

8-3 Something ***could have been*** stolen.

這句話的意思是「可能會有東西被偷。」文雅的說法是：Something might have been taken. (可能會有東西被拿走。) 也可說成：Something could have gone missing. (東西可能會不見。)

8-4　My key *went missing*.
　　　go missing　不見了

　　　　「我的鑰匙不見了。」的説法還有：I lost my key.
　　（我遺失了我的鑰匙。）或 I couldn't find my key.
　　（我找不到我的鑰匙）或 My key disappeared.（我的
　　鑰匙不見了。）

8-5　My friend helped me find it.

　　　　help 接受詞後，有 to 沒 to 都可以，但現代英文多
　　不用 to。這句話也可説成：My friend helped me
　　locate it.（我的朋友幫我找到它。）
　　【locate〔'loket , lo'ket〕v. 找到】

8-6　I gave him a nice *reward*.
　　　reward〔rɪ'wɔrd〕n.v. 報酬；獎賞

　　　　這句話的意思是「我給他一個很好的報酬。」也可説
　　成：I rewarded him.（我給他報酬。）或 I gave him
　　a gift to show my appreciation.（我給他一個禮物表達
　　我的感激。）【appreciation〔ə,priʃɪ'eʃən〕n. 感激】

8-7　*Having spent all your money*, you couldn't *afford to* eat.
　　　afford〔ə'fɔrd〕v. 負擔得起

　　　　這句話源自：As you had spent all your money,
　　you couldn't afford to eat.（因爲你花光所有的錢，所以

你沒錢吃飯。）也可說成：Having used up all your money, now you're too broke to eat.（因為你用光所有的錢，你現在窮到沒飯吃了。）【use up 用完】

8-8 I was *broke*, too.

　　broke 是形容詞，作「沒錢的」解。

　　「我也沒錢。」的說法還有：I had no money, either. 句中 too 和 either 前有沒有逗點都可以。

　　這句話也可說成：I was also penniless.（我也身無分文。）【penniless〔'pɛnɪlɪs〕adj. 身無分文的】

8-9 *Otherwise*, I would have helped you.

　　Otherwise（否則）代替 If 子句，在這裡等於 If I had not been broke。這句話等於 If I had not been broke, I would have helped you.（如果不是我沒錢的話，我就會幫你。）

> 　　這句話是假設法的過去式，表示「與過去事實相反」，有時，if 子句可用其他用法代替，如：
> *A Chinese* would not do so.【名詞片語代替 If 子句】
> = *If he were a Chinese*, he would not do so.
> （如果是中國人，就不會那麼做。）
> 【詳見「文法寶典」p.365 看不見的 If 子句】

9. *How was your day?*

How was your day?	你今天過得怎樣？
What was the *highlight*?	你今天什麼事情最特別？
Anything interesting?【2014 北京】	有什麼有趣的事情？
Once you *start eating less*, your weight will drop.【2014 天津】	一旦你開始少吃，你的體重就會下降。
Keeping it off is difficult.	減輕體重很難。
You must *stick it out*.	你必須要堅持到底。
You have helped me *greatly*.【2014 江蘇】	你幫了我很多。
You've assisted me *in many ways*.	你在很多方面協助過我。
I'*m indebted to* you.	我很感謝你。

** ────────────

highlight〔'haɪ,laɪt〕*n.* 最精彩的部分

once〔wʌns〕*conj.* 一旦

weight〔wet〕*n.* 體重　　drop〔drɑp〕*v.* 下降

keep it off 減輕體重　　***stick it out*** 堅持到底

assist〔ə'sɪst〕*v.* 協助

indebted〔ɪn'dɛtɪd〕*adj.* 欠債的；感謝的

【背景説明】

你和朋友度過美好的一天，要離開時，你該説些什麼話？事先有準備，你説出來就好聽，人人喜歡你。

9-1 *How was* your day?

> 美國人的習慣是，看到朋友旅遊回來會問：*How was your trip?*（你的旅行如何？）放學回家媽媽會問：*How was school?*（學校怎麼樣？）先生下班回家，太太通常也會問：*How was work?*（工作進行得如何？）最常説的是：*How was your day?*（你今天過得怎樣？）和 Did you have a good day?（你今天過得好嗎？）

9-2 What was the *highlight*?

highlight〔'haɪ‚laɪt〕 *n.* 最精彩的部分；（電視）精彩片段

highlight 字面意思是「強光」，引申爲「強光的效果；最精彩、最重要、最突出、最有趣的部分」，如 the *highlight* of the evening（晚會的高潮）、the *highlight* of the trip（旅行中最難忘的部分）。What was the *highlight*? 在這裡指「你今天什麼事情最特別？」

highlight 就像圖中燈光打下來，突顯目標。

9-3 *Anything interesting?*

> anything 後面加形容詞，形成慣用句，如：
> *Anything new?*（有什麼新鮮事？）
> *Anything special?*（有什麼特別的事？）
> *Anything cool?*（有什麼很酷的事？）

【比較】 Anything interesting?【最常用】
（有什麼有趣的事情？）
Anything interesting happen?【第二常用】
（有什麼有趣的事情發生？）
Anything interesting happen today?【第三常用】
（今天有什麼有趣的事情發生？）
Did anything interesting happen today?
（今天有什麼有趣的事情發生？）【第四常用，正式】

如果不知道 Anything interesting happen? 是一個省略句，你就不敢說出來，會錯誤說出 *Anything interesting happened?*（誤），錯把 Anything interesting 當主詞，動詞用過去式。

9-4 Once you ***start eating less***, your weight will drop.

可說成：Your weight will drop when you start eating less.（當你開始少吃的時候，你的體重就會下降。）
(= *Your weight will drop when you eat less.*)

9-5 *Keeping it off* is difficult.

keep off 字面意思是「避開」，如：Keep off the grass.（不要踐踏草地。）在本句中，keep it off 是指 keep the weight off (*your body*)。這句話源自：
Keeping your weight off (*your body* 不用) is difficult.
在這裡 it 不指「食物」。如果要「遠離食物」，要說成：
Staying away from food is difficult.（遠離食物很難。），
不可說成：*Keeping off food is difficult.*（誤）。

9-6　You must *stick it out*.

　　　stick it out 意思是「堅持到底」這句話也可說成：
You must stick to it. (你必須堅持。) 或 You must
stick to your guns. (你必須堅持立場。)「堅持到底」
的同義句很多，詳見「一口氣背同義字寫作文」p.26。

9-7　You have helped me *greatly*.

　　　還可說成：You have helped me a lot. (你幫了我
很多。) (= *You have helped me a great deal.*) 也可用
過去式，說成：You helped me greatly.

9-8　You've assisted me *in many ways*.

　　　可加強語氣說成：You've assisted me in a bunch
of different ways. (你在很多方面協助過我。) (= *You
have helped me in a bunch of different ways.*) 也可用
過去式，說成：You assisted me in many ways.

9-9　I'*m indebted to* you.

　　　debt 是「債務」，indebted 就是「欠債的」，*be
indebted to sb.* 字面意思是「欠某人債務」，引申為「感
謝某人」。可說成：I'm deeply in your debt. (我非常感
謝。) 或 I'm forever indebted to you. (我永遠感謝你。)
所有感謝的話在「演講式英語」p.301 都有。

一口氣考試英語 Unit 4

※ 以三組為一個單位較好背。

1. *Make yourself at home*.
   You can *ask* anyone *for* help.
   【2014 安徽】
   Everyone here is willing to *lend you a hand*. 【2014 安徽】

   Our business is *growing*.
   We are starting to *make a profit*.
   But there are still many problems *to be solved*.

   Stay on track.
   Don't *get distracted*.
   You will never gain success unless you *are devoted*. 【2014 湖南】

2. Do your best to *perform* your *duty*. 【2014 安徽】
   Be an *example* for others to *follow*.
   Wait for the opportunity to *get promoted*. 【2014 安徽】

   Seek challenges.
   Start your own business.
   You can *achieve independence*.
   【2014 江西】

   What *makes for* a happy life?
   【2014 湖南】
   To do what we love is not enough.
   We must like the things we have to do.

3. I always *go jogging* in the morning. 【2014 江蘇】
   I usually *do push-ups* as well.
   【2014 江蘇】
   My goal is to *stay in shape*.
   【2014 江蘇】

   It's *quite hot* today. 【2014 陝西】
   The weekend is approaching.
   Do you *feel like* going for a swim?

   Do you *play badminton*? 【2014 安徽】
   It's my favorite sport.
   Would you like to play sometime?

   * * *

4. *I have been trying to phone Tom*.
   【2014 湖北】
   There *must be* something wrong with the network. 【2014 湖北】
   I can't seem to *get through*.
   【2014 湖北】

   Tom is away from home *quite a bit*. 【2014 全國大綱】
   He *seldom* sees his family.
   【2014 全國大綱】
   He misses his children.

   He is thought *to have acted* foolishly. 【2014 江西】
   Now, he is out of a job.
   He has *no* one to blame *but himself*. 【2014 江西】

5. This is the village *where* I was born.
   【2014 陝西】
   Now it has *grown into* a town.
   【2014 陝西】
   In addition to the school, the village has a clinic. 【2014 陝西】

   The forest park is *far away*. 【2014 北京】
   It is not easy to *get to*.
   The road to *get there* is dangerous.

   I can't meet you on Sunday. 【2014 江蘇】
   I'll be *otherwise* occupied. 【2014 江蘇】
   Maybe next time we can meet.

6. I'll check my schedule.
   Call me tomorrow. 【2014 全國大綱】
   I'll let you know *when I am free*.
   【2014 全國大綱】

   I've *prepared* all kinds of food *for* the picnic. 【2014 湖南】
   There's no need to bring anything.
   We'll have a wonderful time.

   Excuse me.
   I'd like your attention.
   Please *look up from* your cell phone.
   【2014 安徽】

   　　 ＊　　＊　　＊

7. *The book was published 30 years ago*.
   It is still popular. 【2014 安徽】
   It has *stood the test of time*. 【2014 安徽】

   Every class is exciting.
   First, a lecture is given. 【2014 江蘇】
   Then, a lively *question-and-answer session* follows. 【2014 江蘇】

※ 可將這兩頁用手機拍下來背。

I like *lying on the grass*.
【2014 湖南】
I enjoy *staring at* the night sky.
【2014 湖南】
There is *no greater* pleasure *than* being outdoors. 【2014 湖南】

8. *Dear me!* 【2014 江蘇】
   Somebody has *left the door open*. 【2014 江蘇】
   Something *could have been* stolen.

   My key *went missing*.
   【2014 全國大綱】
   My friend helped me find it.
   I gave him a nice *reward*.

   Having spent all your money, you couldn't *afford to* eat.
   【2014 江西】
   I was *broke*, too.
   Otherwise, I would have helped you.

9. *How was* your day?
   What was the *highlight*?
   Anything interesting? 【2014 北京】

   Once you *start eating less*, your weight will drop. 【2014 天津】
   Keeping it off is difficult.
   You must *stick it out*.

   You have helped me *greatly*.
   【2014 江蘇】
   You've assisted me *in many ways*.
   I'*m indebted to* you.

九句話解決你一生的問題！

很多人問我如何成功？年輕人沒錢，怎麼發財？大學畢業後，在這個社會上如何生存下去？我最近教「一口氣考試英語」，出題教授不經意地把他們成功的經驗放在考題中，他們告訴年輕人，剛出社會要：

1. Stay on track.（做正確的事。）
2. Don't get distracted.（不要分心。）
3. You will never gain success unless you are devoted.
   （除非你全心投入，否則你不會獲得成功。）【2014 湖南】

有些年輕人畢業後，東想西想，沒有在正確的軌道（track）上，所謂「正確的軌道」就是做大部份人該做的事，不要去參與示威遊行抗議之類的事，讓自己分心。如當一個英文老師，就要盡全力把學生教好，教到學生為你瘋狂，不要分心去做亂七八槽的事。專心做一件事，什麼事都能成功。到了一家公司，不管做什麼職位，都要：

4. Do your best to perform your duty.【2014 安徽】
   （盡力做好你的職責。）
5. Be an example for others to follow.
   （做一個讓別人可以效法的榜樣。）
6. Wait for the opportunity to get promoted.【2014 安徽】
   （等待升遷的機會。）

老師的同學魏道榮董事長，當年沒有讀大學，身無分文夜宿台北火車站，他從報紙上看到有間電子工廠徵工人，到了工廠上班後，專心上班，做別人不願意做的事，把工廠的事當作自己的事，後來當了工頭，表現良好，接著當了廠長，現在是上櫃公司的大董事長。世界上沒有做不到的事，看他的氣質，看不出來是工人出身。

7. Seek challenges. （尋找挑戰。）

8. Start your own business. （要自行創業。）

9. You can achieve independence.

（你可以獲得獨立。）【2014 江西】

　　上面簡簡單單的九句話，就指出了「成功之道」。成功就是這麼簡單：努力工作→成為領導人物→自行創業。這樣還不夠，該怎麼樣才能過快樂的生活？

What makes for a happy life?【2014 湖南】

（什麼有助於快樂的生活？）

To do what we love is not enough.【2014 湖南】

（做我們所喜愛的事是不夠的。）

We must like the things we have to do.【2014 湖南】

（我們必須喜歡我們必須做的事。）

出題教授好厲害！以前，我只知道：Do what you love. Love what you do. Big money will follow you. 不曉得我們必須喜歡我們必須做的事。當學生的時候，你要喜歡讀書，要喜歡考試；當老師的話，就要喜歡教書。有寬大的心胸愛周圍的人，你自己最受益，抱怨將帶來身心的傷害。

　　我最快樂的事，就是把這項新發明傳授給大家。傳統的學英文方法，是一學期讀 12 篇文章，翻來覆去地研究 12 篇文章。大部份的人即使大學畢業，也不會說英文，表示這種方法是錯誤的。其實，只要背了「一口氣英語」，馬上就會說英文，會說又會寫。現在發明的「一口氣考試英語」是「一口氣英語」的進階版，背完後，讓你會考試，也讓你說得比美國人好。

劉毅

UNIT 5　1~3劇情簡介

【詢問別人想法，要不要吃飯】

1. ***What are you thinking?***
   What's on your mind?
   A penny for your thoughts.

I'll tell you later.
（我待會會告訴你。）

How hungry are you?
Do you want a big meal?
Let's try all the local snacks
　　my friend recommended.

I'm starving.
（我快餓死了。）

I'm sorry for breaking the cup.
Let me pay for it.
How much did it cost?

Don't worry
about it.
（別擔心。）

*　　*　　*

【提到媽媽，想起小時候】

2. ***I guess Mom is not coming.***
   She is usually so thoughtful.
   If she were coming, she
   　　would have called me.

I wonder where
she is.
（不知道她在哪裡。）

I still remember my happy
childhood.
Mother would take me to the
park.
We always played hide and seek.

What a nice
memory!
(真是美好的回憶！)

You're absent-minded.
Don't rely on your memory.
Write it down before you forget.

I will.
(我會的。)

* * *

【勸告朋友避免甜食、多微笑】

3. ***There is new research out
on cancer.***
Studies show sugar might
be a cause.
Most cancers come from sweets.

I didn't know that.
(那我倒不知道。)

Avoid sweets as much as you can.
Every time you eat sweets, drink
green tea.
This will wash away the sugar.

Really?
(真的嗎？)

I agree.
(我同意。)

Laughter is the best medicine.
A smile can brighten up a day.
It costs nothing but makes people happy.

1. *What are you thinking?*

What are you *thinking*?	你在想什麼？
What's *on your mind*?	你心裡在想什麼？
A penny for your thoughts.	你呆呆地在想什麼？
How hungry are you?	你有多餓？
Do you want a *big meal*?	你要不要大吃一頓？
Let's try all the *local snacks* my friend recommended. 【2014 陝西】	我們試試我朋友推薦的，當地所有的小吃吧。
I'm sorry for breaking the cup. 【2014 全國大綱】	很抱歉我打破了杯子。
Let me *pay for* it.	讓我來賠償。
How much did it *cost*?	它值多少錢？

＊＊

on one's mind 腦中一直想著；為某事操心
penny〔'pɛnɪ〕 *n.* 一分錢
A penny for your thoughts. 你呆呆地在想什麼？
　　【對沈思不語者的問話】
big〔bɪg〕 *adj.* 豐盛的　　meal〔mil〕 *n.* 一餐
local〔'lokl〕 *adj.* 當地的　　snack〔snæk〕 *n.* 小吃
recommend〔,rɛkə'mɛnd〕 *v.* 推薦
pay for 付…的錢；賠償

【背景説明】

　　　　下面九句話天天都可以用得到。和朋友在
一起，你就可以説：What are you thinking?
What's on your mind? 美國人常幽默地説：
A penny for your thoughts.

1-1　What are you *thinking*?

　　　　這句話也可説成：What are you thinking about?
（你在想什麼？）或 Please tell me what you are
thinking about.（請告訴我你在想什麼。）

1-2　What's *on your mind*?

　　　　這句話的意思是「你心裡在想什麼？」可以加強語
氣説成：I'd love to know what is *on your mind*.
（我想知道你有什麼心事。）不可説成：*What's in your
mind?*（誤），in one's mind 是指「就某人看來」，如：
In my mind, he is a genius.（就我看來，他是個天才。）

看到你的朋友心神不寧時，你也可以説：

What's eating you?（你有什麼心事？）
What's bothering you?（什麼使你煩惱？）
What's troubling you?（你有什麼困擾？）

1-3　*A penny for your thoughts*.

　　　　這句話美國人常説。字面的意思是「我會給你一分
錢，如果你告訴我你在想什麼。」（= *I'll give you a penny*

if you tell me what you're thinking.) ***A penny for***
your thoughts. 很早就有了，説話者願意付錢來知道
你的想法，是一種幽默的語氣，以前的 penny（一分
錢）較值錢，表示 I'll pay you if you tell me what's
on your mind. 可以翻成「我給你錢，你告訴我你在想
什麼。」或「你呆呆地在想什麼？」和 What are you
thinking? 及 What's is on your mind? 意思相同，
都表示「你在想什麼？」但有點開玩笑的味道。句中
thoughts 不可用單數 *thought*（誤）。

1-4　How hungry are you?

　　　這句話的意思是「你有多餓？」也可説成：How
hungry are you feeling right now?（你現在感覺有多
餓？）或 Are you very hungry?（你是不是很餓？）

1-5　Do you want a *big meal*?

　　　可加長爲：Do you want a big meal or a light
snack?（你要吃大餐或清淡的小吃？）big meal 可指「正
式的大餐」，也可指「吃很多」（eat until you are full）。

1-6　Let's try all the *local snacks* *my friend recommended*.

　　　「我們試試我朋友推薦的，當地所有的小吃吧。」
可以簡化爲：Let's taste all the local foods.（我們
嚐一嚐所有當地的食物吧。）或 Let's eat every local
snack.（我們去吃當地的每一種小吃吧。）

snack〔snæk〕*n.* 小吃 的發音不要和 snake〔snek〕
n. 蛇 搞混。中國人沒有 /æ/ 的音，所以記得，唸
〔snæk〕時嘴巴要裂開。

1-7 I'm sorry for breaking the cup.

在餐廳，不小心把杯子打破，就可以説這句話。
可加強語氣説成：I'm so sorry for dropping and
breaking the cup. (我很抱歉，把杯子弄掉並打破了。)
也可説成：I apologize for breaking your cup. (我很
抱歉把你的杯子打破了。)
【apologize〔ə'pɑlə,dʒaɪz〕*v.* 道歉】

1-8 Let me *pay for* it.

可更客氣地説：You must let me pay for it. (你
必須讓我來賠償。) 或 Please allow me to pay for it.
(請讓我賠償。)

1-9 How much did it *cost*?

去買東西，問別人多少錢，要説：How much
does it cost? (多少錢？) 根據上下文，這裡要用過去
式，説成：*How much did it cost?* (它值多少錢？)
(= *How much was it?* = *What was it worth?*) 或 How
much should I pay you? (我該付你多少錢？)

2. I guess Mom is not coming.

I *guess* Mom is not coming. 【2014 全國大綱】	我猜想媽媽不來了。
She is usually so *thoughtful*.	她通常非常體貼。
If she *were coming*, she would have called me. 【2014 全國大綱】	如果她要來，她會打電話給我。
I still remember my happy childhood. 【2014 四川】	我仍然記得我快樂的童年。
Mother *would take* me to the park. 【2014 四川】	媽媽常常帶我到公園。
We always played *hide and seek*.	我們總是玩捉迷藏遊戲。
You're *absent-minded*.	你很健忘。
Don't *rely on* your memory.	不要靠你的記憶。
Write it down *before you forget*. 【2014 重慶】	在你忘掉以前，把它寫下來。

**

Mom〔mɑm〕*n.* 媽媽　　thoughtful〔ˈθɔtfəl〕*adj.* 體貼的
childhood〔ˈtʃaɪld͵hʊd〕*n.* 童年
seek〔sik〕*v.* 尋找　　*hide and seek* 捉迷藏
absent-minded〔ˈæbsn̩tˈmaɪndɪd〕*adj.* 心不在焉的；記性差的
rely on 依賴；依靠　　memory〔ˈmɛmərɪ〕*n.* 記憶力

【背景說明】

　　　學英文最好的方法是背句子，用背的句子，
說出來、寫出來才有信心，下面九句話是你和朋
友在餐廳談的話。

2-1 **I *guess*** Mom is not coming.

　　　這句話意思是「我猜想媽媽不來了。」也可說成：
I don't think Mom will show up. (我想媽媽不會出
現。) 或 I doubt Mom will come. (我懷疑媽媽會來。)
(= *I don't believe Mom will come.*)

2-2 She is usually so ***thoughtful***.

　　　也可說成：She is usually very considerate. (她
通常非常體貼。) 或 She is a thoughtful person. (她
非常體貼。)

2-3 If she ***were coming***, she would have called me.

　　　不要被傳統文法「與過去事實相反」的公式限制。

$$\text{傳統文法：If + S + had p.p.}\cdots, \text{S} + \left\{\begin{array}{l}\text{would}\\\text{could}\\\text{should}\\\text{might}\end{array}\right.$$

$$+ \text{ have + p.p.}$$

出題者眞厲害，能夠找到傳統文法規則的盲點，這個公式只是部份適用，新的方法是：**If 子句表過去，用 had p.p.**，表現在或未來，用過去式，和主要子句可分開來思考，只要句意合理，時態可以混合使用。

這句話的 If 子句，were coming 表「與未來事實相反」，因爲 come 是來去動詞，可用進行式表未來，主要子句 would have called 表「與過去事實相反」，這句話是根據上下文判斷，意思是「我認爲她不會來，因爲她沒有打電話給我。」(= *I don't think she will come, because she didn't call me.*)

這句話套公式就變成：*If she had come, she would have called me.* (誤) 句意錯誤，如果硬要用假設法過去式，就要改成：If she had decided to come, she would have called me. (如果她決定要來，她就會打電話給我。) 這個句子就是典型的假設法過去式。

2-4 I *still* remember my happy childhood.

也可說成：I'll never forget my happy early years.
(我永遠不會忘掉我快樂的童年。)

2-5 Mother *would take* me to the park.

would 表示「過去的習慣」，也可說成：Mother *often took* me to the park. (媽媽常帶我去公園。)

Mother 和 Mom 也可說成 My mom 或 My mother (我媽媽)。

2-6 We *always* played *hide and seek*.

這句話是「我們總是玩捉迷藏遊戲」。美國小孩和我
們玩得差不多,他們喜歡玩 hopscotch〔'hɑpˌskɑtʃ〕 *n.*
跳房子,swing 盪秋千,seesaw 翹翹板,slide 溜滑梯。

很奇怪,全世界的小孩都差不多,女孩喜歡玩
「扮家家酒」,英文說成 play house,男孩喜歡玩
「警察抓小偷」,英文是 play chase 或是 play cops
and robbers,也喜歡玩「躲避球」(dodge ball)。

2-7 You're *absent-minded*.

absent-minded 心不在焉的;健忘的 (= *absentminded*)

這句話可以說成:You are forgetful. (你很健忘。)
或 You forget things easily. (你很容易忘記東西。)

2-8 Don't *rely on* your memory.

rely on 依賴 (= *depend on*)

這句話也可說成:Don't depend on your
memory. (不要靠你的記憶。) 或 Don't just depend
on memorizing things. (不要只靠著把事情記在腦裡。)

2-9 Write it down *before you forget*.

也可說成:You'd better write it down before
you forget about it. (在你忘掉以前,最好把它寫下來。)

3. A smile can brighten up a day.

There is new research *out* on cancer.	有關癌症的新研究出版了。
Studies show sugar might be a cause.	研究顯示，糖可能是原因之一。
Most cancers come from *sweets*.	大部分癌症來自於甜食。
Avoid sweets as much as you can.	儘量避免甜食。
Every time you eat sweets, drink green tea.【2014 浙江】	每次吃完甜食，要喝綠茶。
This will *wash away* the sugar.	這可以沖掉糖分。
Laughter is the best medicine.	笑是最好的藥。
A smile can *brighten up* a day.	笑容能夠使人有愉快的一天。
It costs nothing *but* makes people happy.【2014 重慶】	不花錢，卻能使人們快樂。

** ——————————————

research〔ˈrɪsɝtʃ〕 *n.* 研究　　out〔aʊt〕 *adv.* 出現

on〔ɑn〕 *prep.* 關於　　cancer〔ˈkænsɚ〕 *n.* 癌症

study〔ˈstʌdɪ〕 *n.* 研究　　sugar〔ˈʃʊgɚ〕 *n.* 糖

cause〔kɔz〕 *n.* 原因　　sweets〔swits〕 *n. pl.* 甜食

as much as one *can* 儘可能（= *as much as possible*）

wash away 沖走；洗掉　　*brighten up* 使明亮；使生色

【背景説明】

最新研究顯示，大部分癌症來自甜食，除了身體健康以外，還有心理的健康，勸人多微笑，不花什麼錢，卻給人快樂。這兩項重要的健康資訊，要傳給你的朋友。考試常考知識性和教育性的句子。

3-1　There is new research *out* on cancer.

句中 out 表示「出版」(= *published*)，on 表示「有關」(= *concerning*)。這句話也可説成：There is new research just out on cancer. (有關癌症的新研究剛剛出版。)

【比較】 *There is a new research.* (誤)
【research (研究) 不可數】
There is a new study. (正)

3-2　*Studies show* sugar might be a cause.

這句話原爲：Studies show sugar might be a cause of cancer. (研究顯示，糖可能是癌症的原因之一。) 也可以説成：These recent studies state that sugar might be a cause of cancer. (這些最近的研究説明，糖可能是癌症的原因之一。)

3-3　Most cancers come from *sweets*.

　　也可說成：A majority of cancers result from sugar products.（大部分癌症起因於含糖的產品。）

3-4　*Avoid* sweets *as much as you can*.

　　也可說成：Avoid sweets as much as possible.（儘量避免甜食。）(= *Stay away from sweets as often as you can*.)

3-5　*Every time* you eat sweets, drink green tea.

　　Every time 是連接詞，引導副詞子句，等於 Whenever。這句話也可說成：After you eat sweets, drink green tea.（吃完甜食後，要喝綠茶。）或 You should drink green tea after eating sugar products.（吃完甜品後，你應該喝綠茶。）

3-6　This will *wash away* the sugar.

　　wash away　沖走；沖掉，這句話也可說成：Doing this will wash away the sugar.（這麼做可以沖掉糖分。）

3-7　Laughter is the best medicine.

　　這句話接上二組，談到癌症，避免罹患癌症的主要方法之一，是保持心情愉快。除了說「笑是最好的藥」以

外,美國人還常說:A smile can lift people up. 字面意思是「微笑可以把人抬起來。」引申爲「笑容能使人高興。」(= *A smile can make people happy.*)

3-8 A smile can *brighten up* a day.

brighten 是「照亮」,brighten up 是加強語氣,可作「照得很亮」解。

> 【比較】 A smile can brighten a day. 【普通語氣】
>
> A smile can brighten up a day. 【加強語氣】

這句話字面意思是「笑容能夠把一天照得很亮」,引申爲「笑容能夠使人有愉快的一天。」美國人喜歡說:Have a good day. (祝你有美好的一天。) I have a good day. 表示「我今天很愉快。」

這句話也可說成:A smile can make a day brighter. (笑容可使一天更美好。) (= *Smiling at people can make a day brighter.*) 或 A smile can make others happy. (笑容可以讓別人快樂。)

3-9 It costs nothing *but* makes people happy.

這句話意思是「不花錢,卻能使人們快樂。」源自 It costs you nothing to give others a smile, but it makes people happy. (對別人微笑不花你一毛錢,卻能使人們快樂。)

UNIT 5 4~6劇情簡介

【提到朋友不舒服，勸人早起運動】

4. *James looks bad.*
   His arrival is a surprise.
   I didn't know he was coming
   until yesterday.

How is he doing now?
（他現在好嗎？）

We must keep an eye on him.
We should carefully observe
   him.
If his condition gets worse, we
   should take him to the hospital.

I hope he gets
well soon.
（希望他早日康復。）

Wake up early every morning.
Get an hour of exercise.
You're guaranteed to sleep well
   at night.

I'll try that.
（我會試試看。）

* * *

【告訴別人你要外出，旅行必帶書】

5. *I'll be out for some time.*
   Please reschedule my appointments.
   In case anything happens, call me
      immediately.

Got it.
（了解。）

I never go traveling without a book.
Reading is the best way to pass time.
I read everything I can to improve
    myself.

That's a good
habit to have.
（那是個好習慣。）

I borrowed a Sherlock Holmes book.
I don't really like the writing style.
I have to admit his stories are
    exciting.

I think so, too.
（我也這麼認為。）

* * *

【敘述自己的震驚，安慰、鼓勵朋友】

6. *I can't believe you did that.*
   I'm both shocked and surprised.
   How could you turn down such
     a fantastic job?

I have my reasons.
（我有我的理由。）

It's not the end of the world.
There is no reason to be
   disappointed.
When one door closes, another
   one opens.

Always look on the
bright side.
（一定要樂觀。）

Face up to your problems.
Don't run away from them.
The best approach is to work
   things out.

Indeed it is.
（確實是。）

4. James looks bad.

James *looks bad*.	詹姆斯看起來很糟糕。
His arrival is *a surprise*.【2014 重慶】	他的來到使我吃驚。
I did*n't* know he was coming *until* yesterday.【2014 重慶】	直到昨天,我才知道他要來。
We must *keep an eye on* him.	我們必須看著他。
We should carefully *observe* him.【2014 北京】	我們應該小心觀察他。
If his condition gets worse, we should *take him to the hospital*.	如果他的情況惡化,我們應該帶他去醫院。
Wake up early every morning.	每天早上早起。
Get an hour of exercise.【2014 安徽】	做一小時運動。
You're guaranteed to sleep well at night.	保證你晚上睡得很好。

** ————————

arrival〔ə'raɪvḷ〕*n.* 到達;來到
surprise〔sə'praɪz〕*n.* 令人驚訝的事
keep an eye on 看著;注意　　observe〔əb'zɝv〕*v.* 觀察
condition〔kən'dɪʃən〕*n.* 情況　　*wake up* 醒來;起牀
guarantee〔͵gærən'ti〕*v.* 保證

【背景説明】

前面兩組談到 James 生病,後面談到治療
失眠的方法是每天早起做運動,晚上就睡得好,
睡得好就不會生病。

4-1 James *looks bad*.

> James〔dʒemz〕*n.* 詹姆斯【人名,注意字尾有 S】

這句話意思是「詹姆斯看起來很糟糕。」也可説成:
James looks ill.(詹姆斯看起來生病了。)(= *James
looks sick.*)還可説成:James looks very unhealthy.
(詹姆斯看起來很不健康。)或 James looks under the
weather.(詹姆斯看起來不太舒服。)

4-2 His arrival is *a surprise*.

這句話也可説成:His arrival surprised me.(他
的來到使我吃驚。)(= *His coming surprised me.*)或
He showed up with little notice.(他沒有提早通知就
出現了。)

4-3 I did*n't* know he was coming *until* yesterday.

這句話意思是「直到昨天,我才知道他要來。」

4-4 We must *keep an eye on* him.

keep an eye on 意思是「看著;注意」(= *watch*)。

也可說成：We must watch him.（我們必須看著他。）

或加強語氣說成：We must carefully watch him.（我們必須小心地看著他。）

4-5　We should carefully *observe* him.

ob ¦ serve　有兩個主要意思：①觀察（眼睛不停地看）
eye ¦ keep　　　　　　　　　②遵守（眼睛要看著）

　　這句話也可說成：We should pay close attention to him.（我們應該密切注意他。）

4-6　*If his condition gets worse*, we should *take him to the hospital*.

　　「帶他去看病」可以用 take him to the hospital（帶他去醫院），take him to the clinic（帶他去診所），或 take him to a doctor 或 take him to the doctor（帶他去看醫生）。

4-7　*Wake up* early *every morning*.

Wake up
Get up　　}　early every morning.　每天早上早起。
Rise

4-8 *Get an hour of* exercise.

也可説成：Work out for an hour.（運動一小時。）

（= *Exercise for an hour.*）美國人「運動」不説 take exercise，而説 *get some exercise* 或 *exercise*。

【比較】 Let's exercise.【第一常用】
= Let's get some exercise.【第二常用】
= Let's do some exercise.【第三常用】
Let's take some exercise.【字典上有，美國人不用】

4-9 *You're guaranteed to* sleep well at night.

這句話的主動是：I guarantee that you will sleep well at night.（我保證，你晚上會睡得很好。）不可説成：*I guarantee you to sleep well at night.*（誤）

be guaranteed to V 已經成爲一個句型，作「保證做某事」解，這個句型你要常用。

You're guaranteed to succeed if you study hard.
（如果你努力用功，保證你會成功。）

You're guaranteed to be healthy if you eat right.
（如果你吃的對，保證你會很健康。）

You're guaranteed to make it big if you stick with me.
（如果你和我在一起，保證你會成功。）

5. *I'll be out for some time*.

I'll be *out* for *some time*. 【2014 四川】	我將出去一段時間。
Please *reschedule* my appointments.	請重新安排我的約會。
In case anything happens, call me immediately. 【2014 四川】	萬一有任何事發生，立刻打電話給我。
I *never* go traveling *without* a book. 【2014 安徽】	我每次旅行必帶一本書。
Reading is the best way to *pass time*. 【2014 安徽】	閱讀是打發時間最好的方法。
I read everything I can to *improve myself*. 【2014 浙江】	為了讓我自己進步，我什麼書都讀。
I borrowed a Sherlock Holmes book. 【2014 北京】	我借了一本福爾摩斯的書。
I don't really like the writing style. 【2014 山東】	我並不怎麼喜歡他的寫作風格。
I have to admit his stories are exciting. 【2014 山東】	我必須承認，他的故事很刺激。

** ───────────────

some time 一段時間　　reschedule〔rɪˋskɛdʒul〕v. 重新安排
appointment〔əˋpɔɪntmənt〕n. 約會　　*in case* 萬一
Sherlock Holmes〔ˋʃɝlɑkˋhomz〕n. 福爾摩斯
admit〔ədˋmɪt〕v. 承認

【背景說明】

　　　　這一回講到出去，要重新安排約會，講到旅行和閱讀，並學二個重要的會話句型：*I don't really like* 和 *I have to admit*。

5-1　I'll be *out for some time*.

　　　　也可說成：I'll be out for a while.（我將出去一會兒。）（= *I'll be out for a short time.*）

5-2　Please *reschedule* my appointments.

　　　　schedule 是「安排」，reschedule 是「重新安排」，如果要「取消約會」，可以說：Please cancel all my appointments.（請取消我所有的約會。）

5-3　*In case anything happens*, call me *immediately*.

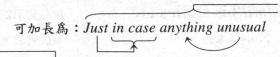

　　　　可加長為：*Just in case anything unusual happens*, call me immediately.（萬一有任何不尋常的事情發生，立刻打電話給我。）美國人也常說：If something happens, let me know as soon as possible.（如果有事情發生，儘快通知我。）

5-4　I *never* go traveling *without* a book.

　　也可説成：I always travel with a book.（我每次
旅行都帶著一本書。）可加長爲：I never go traveling
without a book in my hand.（我每次旅行，手上都拿著
一本書。）

5-5　Reading is the best way to *pass time*.

　　也可説成：Reading is the most beneficial way to
spend time.（閱讀是打發時間最有益的方法。）pass time
（打發時間）也可用 pass the time。這句話可加長爲：
In my opinion, reading is the very best way to pass
the time.（依我之見，閱讀是打發時間最好的方法。）

5-6　I read everything *I can* to *improve myself*.

　　everything I can 源自 everything *that* I can *read*，
關代 that 和 read 省略。

5-7　I borrowed a Sherlock Holmes book.

　　Sherlock Holmes〔'ʃɝlak 'homz〕*n.* 福爾摩斯，
因爲福爾摩斯的書很多，所以可以説 a Sherlock
Holmes book。這句話可加長爲：I borrowed a
Sherlock Holmes book from the library.（我從圖書
館借了一本福爾摩斯的書。）

5-8 I don't really like the writing style.

也可說成：I don't really like the old English writing style. (我不怎麼喜歡老式的英文寫作風格。)

> 可常説 **I don't really like**，比 I don't like 委婉一點，如：
>
> **I don't really like** to eat spicy foods.
> (我不怎麼喜歡吃辣的食物。)
> **I don't really like** to sit by noisy people.
> (我不怎麼喜歡坐在很吵的人旁邊。)
> **I don't really like** to get up too early.
> (我不怎麼喜歡太早起牀。)

5-9 *I have to admit* his stories are exciting.

這句話意思是「我必須承認，他的故事很刺激。」

> **I have to admit** 是一個常用的會話句型，如：
> **I have to admit** she does a good job.
> (我必須承認，她表現得很好。)
> **I have to admit** it was worth it.
> (我必須承認，那很值得。)
> **I have to admit** you are unique.
> (我必須承認，你非常特別。)

6. *It's not the end of the world.*

I can't believe you did that.	我無法相信你那麼做。
I'm *both* shocked *and* surprised.	我非常驚訝。
How could you turn down such a fantastic job? 【2014 浙江】	你怎麼能拒絕這麼棒的工作？
It's not the end of the world.	這不是世界末日。
There is no reason to be disappointed. 【2014 浙江】	你沒有理由失望。
When *one* door closes, *another* one opens.	當一扇門關上，另一扇門就會打開。
Face up to your problems. 【2014 浙江】	要面對你的問題。
Don't *run away from* them. 【2014 浙江】	不要逃避問題。
The best approach is to *work* things *out*. 【2014 浙江】	最好的方法就是把事情解決。

**

shocked〔ʃɑkt〕*adj.* 震驚的　　*turn down* 拒絕（= *refuse*）
fantastic〔fæn'tæstɪk〕*adj.* 很棒的
disappointed〔͵dɪsə'pɔɪntɪd〕*adj.* 失望的
face up to 面對；正視（= *face*）
run away from 逃避（= *avoid*）
approach〔ə'protʃ〕*n.* 方法（= *method*）
work out 解決（問題）

【背景説明】

看到別人有困難，美國人常説：It's not the
end of the world. 勸他們不要失望，總是會有機會
的。When one door closes, another one opens.

6-1 *I can't believe* you did that.

可以加強語氣説成：I just can't believe you
really did that. （我就是無法相信你真的那樣做。）或
What you did really amazes me. （你所做的事真令我
驚訝。）【amaze〔ə'mez〕v. 使驚訝】

6-2 I'm *both* shocked *and* surprised.

由 both…and 連接兩個同義字，有加強語氣的作
用。也可説成：I'm totally amazed. （我非常驚訝。）

> 學會用 *both~and*，你的會話就更進一步了。
>
> I'm *both* happy *and* grateful. （我又快樂又感激。）
>
> I'm *both* satisfied *and* content. （我非常滿足。）
>
> I'm *both* angry *and* upset. （我非常生氣。）
>
> I'm *both* comfortable *and* relaxed.
>
> （我又舒適又輕鬆。）
>
> I'm *both* hungry *and* thirsty. （我又餓又渴。）
>
> I'm *both* excited *and* thrilled. （我非常興奮。）

6-3　*How could you* turn down such a fantastic job?

　　也可説成：How could you refuse such a great offer?（你怎麼能拒絕這麼好的提議？）或 How could you not take such a tremendous job opportunity?（你怎麼能不接受這麼棒的工作機會？）

offer〔ˋɔfɚ〕*n.* 提議

tremendous〔trɪˋmɛndəs〕*adj.* 巨大的；極好的

> *How could you* .... （你怎麼能…）是很好的句型。
>
> *How could you* do this to me?
>
> （你怎麼能這樣子對我？）
>
> *How could you* stand me up?（你怎麼能放我鴿子？）
>
> *How could you* treat an old friend so badly?
>
> （你怎麼能對老朋友這麼糟？）

6-4　*It's not the end of the world*.

　　這句話的意思是「這不是世界末日。」當別人沮喪時，可説這句話來安慰他。也可説：Tomorrow is a new day.（明天又是新的一天。）或 There is always tomorrow.（總是有明天。）或 Don't quit or give up.（不要停止或放棄。）【quit〔kwɪt〕*v.* 停止；放棄】

6-5　*There is no reason* to be disappointed.

　　這句話源自：There is no reason for you to be disappointed.（你沒有理由失望。）可加長為：There is no real reason for you to be so disappointed.（你真的沒有理由如此失望。）

用 *There is no reason to V* 來勸別人。

There is no reason to be upset. (沒有理由生氣。)

There is no reason to lose your temper.

(沒有理由發脾氣。)

There is no reason to skip class. (沒有理由翹課。)

6-6 When *one* door closes, *another* one opens.

這句話源自諺語：When one door shuts, another opens. (一扇門關，另一扇必開；失去一次機會，還有另一次機會。)【shut〔ʃʌt〕v. 關閉】

6-7 *Face up to* your problems.

這句話也可說成：Face your problems. (要面對你的問題。) 或 Try to overcome your troubles. (儘量克服你的困難。)【troubles〔'trʌbḷz〕n. pl. 困難】face up to (面對) 比 face 的語氣強，不能用 face to，face to 指「面向～」，句意不同。

6-8 Don't *run away from* them.

也可說成：Don't avoid them. (不要逃避它們。) 或 Don't fear them. (不要害怕它們。)(= *Don't be afraid of them.*)

6-9 The best approach is to *work* things *out*.

這句話的意思是「最好的方法就是把事情解決。」也可說成：The best method is to solve your problems. (最好的方法就是解決你的問題。)

UNIT 5　7~9劇情簡介

【勸告朋友開車不要超速、超車】

7. ***Don't speed.***
　　You might lose control.
　　You might go off the road
　　　and get killed.

I'm a careful driver.
(我開車很小心。)

　　Never pass on a turn.
　　You can't see another car
　　　coming at you.
　　Most accidents happen that way.

Yes, they do.
(是的，沒錯。)

　　Take your time.
　　I'm in no hurry.
　　I have all day.

I'll be ready
in a minute.
(我馬上就好。)

* * *

【說服朋友當義工、與人分享】

8. ***Everyone should volunteer.***
　　You should get involved in
　　　community activities.
　　You can gain a lot of experience.

And you're helping
others, too.
(你也在幫助別人。)

Share whatever you have with
    your friends.
Don't ask for anything in return.
You will always be happy and
    well-liked.

You're a generous
    person.
(你真是慷慨大方。)

I was overwhelmed.
I needed help.
They were abroad, or they
    would have come to my aid.

I'm sure they
    would have.
(我確信他們會的。)

* * *

【稱讚別人英文很好】

9. *Jeez!*
    Your English is perfect!
    How did you become fluent?

I studied very hard.
(我非常用功。)

What method did you use?
Where did you study?
How long have you been learning
    English?

For six years.
(六年了。)

I can't remember these grammar
    rules.
They're so confusing.
Maybe you can help me.

I'll do my best.
(我會盡力的。)

7. Don't speed.

Don't *speed*.	不要超速。
You might *lose control*.	你可能會失控。
You might *go off the road* and get killed. 【2014 重慶】	你可能會衝出道路而送命。
Never pass *on a turn*.	轉彎處絕對不要超車。
You can't see another car *coming at* you.	你看不到對向來車。
Most accidents happen *that way*.	大部分車禍都是那樣發生的。
Take your time. 【2014 天津】	慢慢來。
I'm in no hurry. 【2014 天津】	我不急。
I have all day.	我時間很多。

**　——————————————

speed〔spid〕v. 加速；超速　　*lose control* 失控
go off the road 離開道路　　pass〔pæs〕v. 超車
turn〔tɜn〕n. 轉彎處　　*take one's time* 慢慢來
in a hurry 匆忙的　　*in no hurry* 不急

【背景説明】

「不要超速」英文是 *"Don't speed."* ，不背你
怎麼會？「不要超車」是 *"Don't pass."* 。有 85% 的
人，在轉彎處超車都撞車，因爲看不到對面來車，
你的朋友在轉彎處超車時，你一定要對他説 : *Don't
pass on a turn* . 可以保住他的生命。

7-1 Don't *speed*.

這句話源自 *Don't* go over the *speed* limit. (不要
超速。) 也可説成 : Don't exceed the speed limit. (不
要超速。) 可加強語氣説成 : No matter what, *don't
speed* . (無論如何不要超速。)

大字典上有 overspeed (超速) 這個字，但美國人不説
Don't overspeed. (誤) 而 Don't speed up. 指「不要加
速。」和 Don't speed. (不要超速。) ，句意不同。

7-2 You might *lose control*.

這句話源自 You might lose control of your car.
(你的車子可能會失控。) 可加長爲 : You might lose
control and crash. (你可能會失控撞車。) 或 You might
lose control of your car and have an accident. (你的
車子可能會失控，出意外。)

7-3 You might *go off the road* and get killed.
go off the road 離開道路

這句話字面意思是「你可能離開道路死掉。」，引申
爲「你可能會衝出道路而送命。」

外國人常說 *You might*，比 You may 客氣，因為 might 是假設法助動詞，表示説話者心中認為不可能。

> *You might* crash. (你可能會撞車。)
> *You might* get killed. (你可能會送命。)
> *You might* get injured. (你可能會受傷。)
> *You might* have an accident. (你可能會出事。)

會説 *You might*，你的會話就更厲害了。

7-4 Never pass *on a turn*.

　　源自 *Never pass* a car *on a turn*. (轉彎處絕對不要超車。) 很多車禍都是因為轉彎處超車發生的，好的司機任何情況下，不會在轉彎處超車。這句話也可説成：You should never ever pass a car on a turn. (你絕不應該在轉彎處超車。) 或 Never try to pass on a turn. (絕對不要想在轉彎處超車。) on a turn 也可用 around a corner。

7-5 You can't see another car *coming at you*.

　　當你在轉彎處超車時，你看不到對向來車。

(= *When you are passing another car on a turn, you can't see the on-coming traffic*.)

7-6 Most accidents happen *that way*.

> that way 源自 *in that way*（誤），在 way 前的介詞現在多省略。也可説成：That is the way most accidents happen.（大部分車禍都是那樣發生的。）
>
> （= *That is how most accidents happen.*）

7-7 Take your time.

> 源自 You can take your time. 字面意思是「你能夠抓住時間」，引申爲「慢慢來。」

7-8 I'm in no hurry.

> 也可説成：I'm not in a hurry.（我不急。）可以加强語氣説成：No hurry at all.（一點都不急。）

7-9 *I have all day.*

> 這句話字面意思是「我有一整天。」引申爲「我時間很多。」也可説成：I have plenty of time.（我有很多時間。）（= *I have a lot of time.*）還可以説：I can wait.（我可以等。）或 I have time to wait.（我有時間等。）I'm willing to wait.（我很願意等。）
>
> 看到別人很忙，你就可以説：Take your time. I'm in no hurry. I have all day.，會讓別人聽了舒服。

8. *Everyone should volunteer*.

Everyone should *volunteer*.	大家都應該自願當義工。
You should *get involved in* community activities. 【2014 福建】	你應該參與社區活動。
You can *gain* a lot of experience.	你可以獲得很多經驗。
Share whatever you have *with* your friends. 【2014 浙江】	和你的朋友分享你所擁有的。
Don't ask for anything *in return*. 【2014 浙江】	不要要求任何的回報。
You will always be happy and *well-liked*.	你一定會很快樂，而且非常受人喜愛。
I was *overwhelmed*.	我被壓得喘不過氣來了。
I needed help.	我需要幫助。
They were abroad, or they would have *come to my aid*. 【2014 浙江】	他們都在國外，否則他們就會來幫助我了。

**

volunteer〔,vɑlən'tɪr〕 *v.* 自願當義工　***get involved in*** 參與
community〔kə'mjunətɪ〕 *n.* 社區　***in return*** 作爲回報
well-liked〔'wɛl'laɪkt〕 *adj.* 深受喜愛的
overwhelm〔,ovɚ'hwɛlm〕 *v.* 壓倒；使不知所措；使無法承受
abroad〔ə'brɔd〕 *adv.* 在國外　　aid〔ed〕 *n.* 幫助
come to *one's* ***aid*** 來幫助某人

【背景説明】

　　　　有錢人的特質，是喜歡和人分享。考題中的句子，很多具有教育性，把這些句子變成會話，非常精彩。像 volunteer 這個字，你不背，怎麼會用？

8-1 Everyone should *volunteer*.

> 　　volunteer 一般作「自願者」解，在這裡是動詞，作「自願」或「自願當義工」(= *come forward as a volunteer*) 解。這句話也可説成：Everyone should volunteer to help others. (每個人都應該自願幫助他人。) 可加長爲：In my opinion, each citizen should volunteer to help others. (依我之見，每個公民都應該自願幫助他人。)
>
> 【比較】 Who volunteers? (有人自願嗎？)【volunteer 是動詞】
>
> 　　　　Any volunteers? (有人自願嗎？)【volunteer 是名詞】

8-2 You should *get involved in* community activities.

　　也可説成：You should take part in community activities. (你應該參加社區活動。)(= *You should participate in community activities.*)

$$\left\{ \begin{array}{l} \text{involve } \textit{oneself} \text{ in 參與【較少用】} \\ = \text{get involved in【常用】} \end{array} \right.$$

$$\left\{ \begin{array}{l} = \text{take part in【最常用】} \\ = \text{participate in【常用】} \end{array} \right.$$

8-3 You can gain a lot of experience.

　　也可説成：You can get a lot of experience. (你可以得到很多經驗。) 或 You can learn a lot of things. (你可以學到很多東西。)

8-4 ***Share*** <u>whatever you have</u> ***with*** *your friends.*

名詞子句

share *sth.* ***with*** *sb.*　和某人分享某物

　　美國人常説：Share what you have. (和別人分享你所擁有的。) Don't be stingy. (不要小氣。) Don't be selfish. (不要自私。) Be generous with your friends. (對朋友要慷慨。)

8-5 Don't ask for anything ***in return***.

ask *sb.* ***for*** *sth.*　向某人要求某物

ask for *sth.*　要求某物　　***in return***.　作爲回報

　　可加強語氣説成：Don't ever ask for anything in return for your kindness. (絶不要因爲你做了好事而要求任何回報。)

8-6 You will *always* be happy and *well-liked*.

　　也可説成：If you do this, you will always be happy and well-liked. (如果你這樣做，你將會快樂而且深受喜愛。)

> 　　「副詞+過去分詞」形成「複合形容詞」，如：well-liked *adj.* 深受喜愛的，well-behaved *adj.* 守規矩的，well-known *adj.* 有名的。【詳見「文法寶典」p.456】

8-7 I was ***overwhelmed***.

overwhelm〔͵ovɚˈhwɛlm〕*v.* 壓倒；使不知所措；無法承受

overwhelm 這個字很難唸，美國人唸這個字時，h 通常不發音，唸成〔‚ovəˈwɛlm〕。音標中的 h，表示可唸可不唸。【詳見「一口氣背 7000 字」p.650】

這個字主要當「壓倒」解釋，引申為「使受不了；使不知所措」。

可加強語氣說成：I was overwhelmed and in trouble. (我被麻煩壓得喘不過氣來。) 也可說成：I was overwhelmed with things to do. (我被要做的事壓得喘不過氣來。) 或 I had too much to handle. (我有太多事而無法應付。)

8-8 I needed help.

可加強語氣說成：I really needed someone to help me. (我真的需要有人幫助。)

8-9 They were abroad, or they would have *come to my aid*.

abroad (在國外) 可改成 overseas 或 out of the country。整句前面可加上 Unfortunately (遺憾的是)(= *Regrettably*)。

come to my aid　來幫助我
= come to my assistance
come to my help (誤，美國人不用)
come to my rescue　來救我

They were abroad 是直說法的過去式，they would have come to my aid 是假設法的過去式，直說法、假設法、時態可混用，不要被公式限制。

9. Jeez!

Jeez!	天啊！
Your English is *perfect*!	你的英文超好的！
How did you become *fluent*?	你是如何變得這麼流利的？
What method did you use?	你用了什麼方法？
Where did you study?	你在哪裡學的？
How long have you been learning English?【2014 天津】	你學英文學了多久？
I can't remember these grammar rules.【2014 福建】	這些文法規則我都記不起來。
They're so *confusing*.	實在是令人混淆。
Maybe you can help me.	也許你可以幫我。

** ——————————

Jeez!〔dʒiz〕*interj.* 天啊！
perfect〔'pɝfɪkt〕*adj.* 完美的；好極了
fluent〔'fluənt〕*adj.* 流利的　　method〔'mɛθəd〕*n.* 方法
grammar〔'græmɚ〕*n.* 文法
confusing〔kən'fjuzɪŋ〕*adj.* 令人混淆的；令人困惑的

【背景説明】

聽到別人英文説得很好,一定要稱讚。用下面
九句稱讚他,他就會佩服你。稱讚越多越好。加上
一些感嘆詞,像 *Jeez!* 之類的更好。

9-1 *Jeez!*

> *Jeez!*〔dʒiz〕(天啊!哎呀!)是 Jesus〔'dʒisəs〕 *n.*
> 耶穌基督 委婉的説法,現在很常用,用來表示非常驚訝
> 或生氣,例如:
>
> *Jeez*, I can't believe it! (天啊!我不敢相信!)
>
> *Jeez*, what a beautiful sunset!
>
> (哎呀!好美的夕陽!)
>
> *Jeez*, that's too expensive! (天啊!太貴了!)
>
> *Jeez*, he talks too much. (天啊!他話太多了!)
>
> 碰到令人驚奇的事,可單獨使用 Jeez! 一個字,其
> 他常用的還有:Wow! (哇!)、Amazing! (真棒!)、
> Fantastic! (真棒!)、Incredible! (真令人難以置信!)
> (= *Unbelievable!*)

9-2 Your English is *perfect*!

碰到英文説得很流利的人,可用這些話來回應他:
Your English is fluent. (你的英文很流利。) You speak
like a native speaker. (你說得像美國人。) Your English
is excellent! (你的英文真棒!) 可加強語氣説成:Your

English is awesome!（你的英文棒極了！）Your English is the best I've ever heard.（你的英文是我聽過最棒的。）

9-3　How did you become *fluent*?

可說成：How did you get fluent?（你是如何變得這麼流利的？）加強語氣說成：How in the heck did you become so fluent?（你到底是怎麼變得這麼流利？）或 How did you learn to speak so fluently?（你是如何學會說得這麼流利？）【in the heck　究竟；到底】

9-4　*What method* did you use?

可加長爲：What learning method did you use to become fluent?（你用了什麼學習的方法才變得這麼流利？）也可說成：How did you do it?（你是怎麼做到的？）Which way did you use?（你用哪一種方法？）

9-5　Where did you study?

可加長爲：Where did you study to speak so well?（你說得那麼好，是在哪裡學的？）也可說：Where did you learn it?（你在哪裡學的？）再加上兩句：Did you go overseas?（你出過國嗎？）Did you study abroad?（你留過學嗎？）

9-6　How long have you been learning English?

可客氣一點說：Do you mind if I ask, "How long have you been learning English?"（你介不介意我問你：

「你學英文多久了？」）也可說：For how long have
you been studying English?（你學英文多久了？）
How many years have you been learning English?
（你學英文多少年了？）

9-7 I can't remember these grammar rules.

可說成：I can't recall these grammar rules.
（我想不起來這文法規則。）或 I forgot these grammar
rules.（我忘了這些文法規則。）

9-8 They're so *confusing*.

可加長為：
To me,
For me,　　⎫
In my opinion,　⎬ they are so confusing.
　　　　　　⎭
（我覺得它們很令人混淆。）

或 They are difficult to understand.（它們很難了解。）

9-9 *Maybe* you can help me.

可說成：Maybe you can give me some help.
（也許你可以給我一些幫助。）Perhaps you could help
me out.（也許你能夠幫我的忙。）Could you please
help me?（能不能請你幫我？）Would you mind
helping me?（你介不介意幫幫我？）

一口氣考試英語 Unit 5

※ 以三組爲一個單位較好背。

1. *What are you thinking?*
   What's *on your mind*?
   A penny for your thoughts.

   How hungry are you?
   Do you want a *big meal*?
   Let's try all the *local snacks* my
   friend recommended. 【2014 陜西】

   I'm sorry for breaking the cup.
   【2014 全國大綱】
   Let me *pay for* it.
   How much did it *cost*?

2. I *guess* Mom is not coming.
   【2014 全國大綱】
   She is usually so *thoughtful*.
   If she *were coming*, she would
   have called me. 【2014 全國大綱】

   I still remember my happy
   childhood. 【2014 四川】
   Mother *would take* me to the
   park. 【2014 四川】
   We always played *hide and seek*.

   You're *absent-minded*.
   Don't *rely on* your memory.
   Write it down *before you forget*.
   【2014 重慶】

3. There is new research *out* on
   cancer.
   Studies show sugar might be a
   cause.
   Most cancers come from *sweets*.

Avoid sweets as much as you
can.
Every time you eat sweets, drink
green tea. 【2014 浙江】
This will *wash away* the sugar.

Laughter is the best medicine.
A smile can *brighten up* a day.
It costs nothing *but* makes
people happy. 【2014 重慶】

*　　*　　*

4. *James looks bad*.
   His arrival is *a surprise*. 【2014 重慶】
   I did*n't* know he was coming
   until yesterday. 【2014 重慶】

   We must *keep an eye on* him.
   We should carefully *observe*
   him. 【2014 北京】
   If his condition gets worse,
   we should *take him to the
   hospital*.

   Wake up early every morning.
   Get an hour of exercise. 【2014 安徽】
   You're guaranteed to sleep well
   at night.

5. I'll be *out* for *some time*.
   【2014 四川】
   Please *reschedule* my
   appointments.
   In case anything happens, call
   me immediately. 【2014 四川】

I *never* go traveling *without* a book.
【2014 安徽】
Reading is the best way to *pass time*.
【2014 安徽】
I read everything I can to *improve myself*. 【2014 浙江】

I borrowed a Sherlock Holmes book.
【2014 北京】
I don't really like the writing style.
【2014 山東】
I have to admit his stories are exciting. 【2014 山東】

6. *I can't believe* you did that.
I'm *both* shocked *and* surprised.
How could you turn down such a fantastic job? 【2014 浙江】

It's not the end of the world.
There is no reason to be disappointed.
【2014 浙江】
When *one* door closes, *another* one opens.

Face up to your problems. 【2014 浙江】
Don't *run away from* them. 【2014 浙江】
The best approach is to *work* things *out*. 【2014 浙江】

* * *

7. *Don't speed.*
You might *lose control*.
You might *go off the road* and get killed. 【2014 重慶】

Never pass *on a turn*.
You can't see another car *coming at* you.
Most accidents happen *that way*.

Take your time. 【2014 天津】
I'm in no hurry. 【2014 天津】
I have all day.

8. Everyone should *volunteer*.
You should *get involved in* community activities.
【2014 福建】
You can *gain* a lot of experience.

Share whatever you have *with* your friends. 【2014 浙江】
Don't ask for anything *in return*. 【2014 浙江】
You will always be happy and *well-liked*.

I was *overwhelmed*.
I needed help.
They were abroad, or they would have *come to my aid*. 【2014 浙江】

9. *Jeez!*
Your English is *perfect*!
How did you become *fluent*?

What method did you use?
Where did you study?
How long have you been learning English? 【2014 天津】

I can't remember these grammar rules. 【2014 福建】
They're so *confusing*.
Maybe you can help me.

※ 可將這兩頁用手機拍下來背。

UNIT 6 1~3劇情簡介

【勸人要堅決、要把握機會】

1. ***Are you sure you can make it?***
   Don't just say it to be nice.
   Don't change your mind at
       the last minute.

I won't.
(我不會的。)

Don't miss the chance.
This is your big opportunity.
It may be years before you
    get another one.

I'll keep that
    in mind.
(我會牢記在心。)

I didn't invite her on purpose.
She's not a social person.
She's a wet blanket.

Good decision.
(好決定。)

* * *

【提到一名害羞的女孩，要辦派對】

2. ***She is a shy person.***
   She is afraid to meet anyone.
   She puts a wall between
       herself and others.

I've noticed that, too.
(我也注意到了。)

Don't worry about finding the location.
I will give you clear directions.
You'll have no trouble getting there.

Great!
(很好。)

The party is in the park.
It is near the main gate.
Opposite is Starbucks.

I know the place.
(我知道那個地方。)

* * *

【期待明天的派對，大家都很愉快】

3. *We have just one more day to go.*
   Tomorrow is a big day.
   I'm really looking forward to it.

Me too.
(我也是。)

It's so noisy here.
I can't hear myself think.
It's driving me crazy.

What?
(什麼？)

The park was packed.
They enjoyed themselves
   in the sunshine.
Everyone had a blast.

Sounds like fun.
(聽起來很有趣。)

1. Don't just say it to be nice.

Are you sure you can *make it*?	你確定你能來嗎？
Don't just say it *to be nice*.	不要說客套話。
Don't change your mind *at the last minute*. 【2015 重慶】	不要到最後改變主意。

Don't *miss the chance*. 【2015 重慶】	不要錯過這個機會。
This is your big opportunity.	這是你大好的機會。
It may be years *before you get another one*. 【2015 重慶】	可能要很多年你才能有另一個機會。

I didn't invite her *on purpose*. 【2015 江蘇】	我故意不邀請她。
She's not a *social person*.	她不善於交際。
She's a *wet blanket*. 【2015 江蘇】	她是一個掃興的人。

** ───────────────

make it 成功；辦到；能來　　miss〔mɪs〕v. 錯過
on purpose 故意地
social〔'soʃəl〕adj. 社交的；善交際的
blanket〔'blæŋkɪt〕n. 毯子
a wet blanket 掃興的人

【背景説明】

　　　和美國人説話，要訓練自己一開口就説三句。
當別人答應了你的要求以後，你可説：***Don't just
say it to be nice.*** 這是多麼好的英文。説話是一種
藝術，我們趁著學英文的機會，訓練自己的口才。

1-1　Are you sure you can *make it*?

　　　Are you sure 後面可接名詞子句。

　　　make it 意思很多，主要的意思是「成功」，還有「辦
到；做好；能來」的意思，這裡作「能來」解。【詳見「一口
氣背會話」p.134】這句話也可説成：Will you be there for
sure?（你確實能參加嗎？）或 Are you definitely coming?
（你是否確定能來？）

1-2　Don't just say it *to be nice*.

　　　美國人有時比較虛僞，常説一些好聽的話，你就可
以説這句話，確保他的諾言能夠實現。也可説成：Don't
just say it to be polite.（不要説客套話。）或 Say what
you mean.（要説眞心話。）(= *Only say it if you mean it.*)

1-3　Don't change your mind *at the last minute*.
　　　at the last minute　在最後一分鐘

也可説成：Don't change your mind later.（以後不要改變主意。）爲了禮貌，可説成：Please don't change your mind.（請不要改變主意。）*at the last minute* 很常用，例如：He always wakes up *at the last minute*.（他總是最後一分鐘才起床。）

1-4　Don't *miss the chance*.

也可説成：　Seize the chance.（抓住機會。）
Seize the opportunity.（把握機會。）
Don't fail to take this chance.
（不要錯過這個機會。）

機會每天都在身旁，美國人常説：Don't let the opportunity get away.（不要讓機會溜走。）

1-5　This is your big opportunity.

也可説成：This is your big chance.（這是你大好的機會。）（= *This is a great chance for you.*）可加強語氣説成：This is a very important opportunity for you.（這是你非常重要的機會。）

1-6　It may be years *before you get another one*.

句中的 may 可改成 might。也可説成：It may be a long time before you get another one.（可能要很長的時

間，你才有另一個機會。）或 It may be years before a chance like this comes again.（可能要很多年，才會再有像這樣的機會。）也可簡單地說：Opportunities like this don't come often.（像這樣的機會不常有。）

1-7　I didn't invite her *on purpose*.

on purpose 故意地（= *deliberately*）

　　這句話也可說成：I *deliberately* did not invite her.（我故意不邀請她。）不可說成：*I didn't invite her deliberately.*【書本英語】

1-8　She's not a *social person*.

　　也可說成：She's not a sociable person.（她不善交際。）可簡單說成：She's not sociable.（她不會交際。）（= *She's not social.*）

social 和 sociable 在此意義相同，都等於 friendly。

1-9　She's a *wet blanket*.

a wet blanket 掃興的人（= *a person that keeps others from enjoying life*）

　　這句話也可說成：She's not easy to get along with.（她不容易相處。）

2. *The party is in the park*.

She is *a shy person*.【2015 北京】	她很害羞。
She is afraid to meet anyone.【2015 北京】	她怕見任何人。
She *puts a wall* between herself and others.	她不喜歡和別人交際。
Don't worry about *finding the location*.【2015 北京】	不要擔心找不到地點。
I will give you clear directions.【2015 北京】	我會給你明確的說明。
You'll have *no trouble getting there*.【2015 北京】	你到那裡沒問題。
The party is in the park.	派對是在公園內。
It is near the main gate.	靠近大門。
Opposite is Starbucks.【2015 北京】	對面是星巴克。

** ────────────

shy〔ʃaɪ〕*adj.* 害羞的　　location〔loˈkeʃən〕*n.* 地點
directions〔dəˈrɛkʃənz〕*n. pl.* 指示；說明
main gate 大門　　opposite〔ˈɑpəzɪt〕*adj.* 對面的

【背景説明】

　　「一口氣滿分寶典」中的每一句話，都設定在隨時可以説出來，有使用才不會忘記。句子從試題中改編出來，背了以後，看到題目，都是熟悉的句子。

2-1　She is *a shy person*.

　　可簡單説成：She is shy.（她很害羞。）She is very quiet.（她很安靜。）She is not a person person.（她不喜歡和人來往。）(= *She is not a people person*.)

2-2　She is afraid to meet anyone.

　　可説成：She fears meeting anyone.（她害怕見任何人。）或 She doesn't like meeting new people.（她不喜歡見新來的人。）

2-3　She *puts a wall* between herself and others.

　　這句話字面的意思是「她在她和別人之間放一道牆。」引申為「她不喜歡和別人交際。」可加強語氣説成：She *puts up a wall* between herself and others. 意思相同。句中的 a wall 可改成 a curtain（窗簾）。可幽默地説：She *puts a mountain* in front of everyone.（她不願意見任何人。）

2-4 Don't worry about *finding the location*.

可縮短為：Don't worry about the location.（不要擔心地點。）也可說成：Don't worry about finding the address.（不要擔心找不到地點。）

2-5 I will give you clear directions.

可加強語氣說成：I will give you *clear-cut* directions to get there.（我會給你到達那裡明確的方向。）也可簡單說成：I will show you how to get there.（我將告訴你如何到那裡。）【clear-cut〔͵klɪrˈkʌt〕*adj.* 明確的】

2-6 You'll have *no trouble getting there*.

have {
trouble
difficulty
problems
} + (*in*) + V-ing　做…有困難

也可說成：You'll have no difficulty getting there.（你到那裡沒問題。）句中 difficulty 可改成 problems。可簡單說成：You'll get there easily.（你很容易到那裡。）或 You'll find it no problem.（你一定可以找到。）

2-7 The party is in the park.

也可說成：The party will be in the park.（派對將在公園舉行。）（= *The party will be held in the park.*）

2-8 It is near the main gate.

　　也可説成：It is near the main entrance.（它靠近
大門。）(= *It is near the front entrance.*)

2-9 *Opposite is* Starbucks.

> 　　這句話是倒裝句，等於 Starbucks is opposite.
> （星巴克在對面。）【Star（星星）+ bucks（美元）】可加
> 長爲：Opposite the party is Starbucks coffee shop.
> （派對的對面是星巴克咖啡店。）(= *Starbucks coffee
> shop is opposite the party.*)
>
> 有時會爲了強調補語而倒裝，例如：
>
> *Happy* is he *who has a sound mind in a sound body.*
>
> = He *who has a sound mind in a sound body* is happy.
>
> = He is happy *who has a sound mind in a sound body.*
> （有健全身心的人才會快樂。）
> 【詳見「文法寶典」p.636】

3. Everyone had a blast.

We have just *one more day to go*.【2015 四川】	我們只剩下一天。
Tomorrow is *a big day*.	明天是個大日子。
I'm really *looking forward to* it.	我真的很期待。
It's so noisy here.【2015 浙江】	這裡太吵雜了。
I can't *hear myself think*.【2015 浙江】	吵翻天了。
It's *driving me crazy*.	快要使我發瘋了。
The park was *packed*.【2015 北京】	公園擠滿了人。
They enjoyed themselves *in the sunshine*.【2015 北京】	他們在陽光下很愉快。
Everyone *had a blast*.	每個人都玩得很愉快。

** ——————————————

to go 剩下的 (= *left*)
look forward to 期待   noisy〔'nɔɪzɪ〕*adj.* 吵雜的
I can't hear myself think. 吵翻天了；吵得不得了。
drive sb. crazy 使某人發瘋
packed〔pækt〕*adj.* 擠滿人的；擁擠的；爆滿的
enjoy oneself 玩得愉快
in the sunshine 在陽光下 (= *in the sun*)
blast〔blæst〕*n.* 歡樂；滿足   *have a blast* 玩得很愉快

【背景説明】

　　　　背短句是學説英文最快的方法。這九句話常
常用得到。一般人只會説：It's so noisy here.
你可以接著説：I can't hear myself think.　It's
driving me crazy.

3-1　We have *just **one more day to go***.

> 　　one more day 是「還有一天」，two more days 是
> 「還有兩天」。這句話常簡化成：*Just one more day to
> go*. (只剩下一天。) 或 *Just one more day*. (只要再一
> 天。) 可加長為：We have just one more day to go
> before the party. (在派對前，我們只剩下一天。) 句中
> 的 just 等於 only。也可説成：Only one more day to
> go. (還剩下一天。) to go 在此是「剩下的」，所以也可
> 説成：Only one day left. (只剩下一天。)

3-2　Tomorrow is *a big day*.

　　　　字面的意思是「明天是個大日子。」引申為「明天很
重要。」(= *Tomorrow is very important*.) 或 Tomorrow
is a very special day. (明天是個非常特別的日子。) 也可
説成：Tomorrow will be a big day. 不一定未來時間一
定要用未來式，所以，**背句子最安全**。

3-3　I'm *really **looking forward to*** it.

　　　　look forward to「期待」，to 是介系詞。也可説成：
I can't wait for it. (我迫不及待。) 或 I'm really excited
about it. (對於這件事我真的很興奮。)

3-4 It's *so* noisy here.

　　可加長為：It's so noisy here that I can't hear a thing. (這裡很吵，我什麼都聽不到。) 也可說成：There is much noise here. (這裡有太多吵雜聲。) (= *There is a lot of noise here.*)

3-5 I can't *hear myself think*.

> 　　這句話字面的意思是「我沒辦法聽到我自己想。」自己想什麼，自己知道，但是太吵了，連想什麼都不知道，這是一種誇張的表達方法，強調這個環境很吵。這句話相當於中文的「吵翻天了。」可加長為：It's so noisy here, I can't hear myself think. (這裡太吵了。) 也可說成：It's difficult to hear well. (很難聽清楚。) (= *It's tough to listen clearly.*) 【tough〔tʌf〕*adj.* 困難的】不能說成：*I can't hear myself speak.* (誤)

3-6 It's *driving me crazy*.

　　drive 的主要意思是「開車載 (某人)」，在這裡作「驅使；迫使」解。

drive sb. crazy 使某人發瘋 (= *drive sb. mad*)

　　這句話的意思是「快要使我發瘋了。」也可說成：It's making me feel crazy. (快要使我發瘋了。)

(= *It's making me insane.*)

【insane〔ɪn'sen〕*adj.* 瘋狂的】

3-7 The park was *packed*.

packed〔pækt〕*adj.* 擠滿人的；擁擠的；爆滿的

　　pack 的主要意思是「打包；捆紮」，這句話字面的意思是「這個公園已經被捆紮了。」引申為「這個公園很擁擠。」【詳見「一口氣背會話」p.864】(= *The park was crowded.*) 也可說成：The park was full of people.（這個公園充滿了人。）

3-8 They enjoyed themselves *in the sunshine*.

　　也可說成：They enjoyed themselves in the sun.（他們在陽光下玩得很愉快。）(= *They had a good time in the sunshine.*)

> *enjoy oneself* 玩得愉快
> = *have fun*
> = *have a good time*

3-9 Everyone *had a blast*.

　　blast 的主要意思是「爆炸」，在此作「歡樂；滿足」解。

> *Everyone had a blast.*（每個人都玩得很愉快。）
> = Everyone had a ball.
> = Everyone had a great time.
> = Everyone had a really good time.

ball〔bɔl〕*n.* 球；舞會；愉快的時刻　　have a ball 玩得很愉快

UNIT 6 4~6劇情簡介

【提到派對、稱讚朋友博學多聞】

4. ***We totally enjoyed the party.***
   We were treated so well.
   It was an unforgettable
      occasion.

Indeed, it was.
(的確是。)

You seem so excited.
Fill me in.
Tell me what happened.

It's kind of a long story.
(說來有一點話長。)

You are well-read.
You're interesting to talk with.
You're always full of good
   ideas.

Thanks
(謝謝。)

* * *

【提到朋友要來、開會事宜】

5. ***Tom is coming next month.***
   Let's find out his arrival date.
   We need to book a room for him.

Agreed.
(同意。)

The meeting will be held in
 September.
It is scheduled to be in Shanghai.
I don't know the exact date for
 sure.

You'd better
 find out soon.
(你最好快點找出來。)

I can't attend the meeting.
I will be teaching a class at
 that time.
Let me know what I miss.

I will.
(我會的。)

＊　＊　＊

【提醒朋友搭飛機應注意的事】

6. *We are catching the first flight.*
 We need to get up early.
 We must order a taxi in advance.

Let's do that.
(我們就這麼做。)

Don't sit too long.
Get up and stretch your legs.
Good circulation is essential.

Great advice.
(好建議。)

Be careful with the camera.
Don't drop it.
It costs an arm and a leg.

Don't worry.
(別擔心。)

4. You are well-read.

We *totally enjoyed* the party. 【2015 北京】	我們非常喜歡這個派對。
We were *treated* so *well*.【2015 北京】	我們被招待得很周到。
It was *an unforgettable occasion*.	它是個令人難忘的場合。
You *seem so excited*.【2015 天津】	你似乎很興奮。
Fill me in.	告訴我詳情。
Tell me *what happened*.	告訴我發生了什麼事。
You are *well-read*.	你很有學問。
You're interesting *to talk with*.	和你談話很有趣。
You're always *full of good ideas*. 【2015 四川】	你總是有很多好點子。

** ─────────────────

totally〔ˈtotḷɪ〕*adv.* 完全地；非常

treat〔trit〕*v.* 對待；招待

unforgettable〔ˌʌnfɚˈgɛtəbḷ〕*adj.* 令人難忘的

occasion〔əˈkeʒən〕*n.* 場合　　*fill sb. in* 告訴某人詳情

well-read〔ˈwɛlˈrɛd〕*adj.* 博覽群書的；博學的

be full of 充滿了

【背景説明】

說話是一種藝術，稱讚別人越多越好。好聽的
話要常說，不好聽的話儘量不要講。

4-1 We *totally enjoyed* the party.

這句話也可說成：We totally enjoyed ourselves
at the party. (我們在派對中玩得非常愉快。)
totally〔'totlɪ〕*adv.* 完全地（= *completely* = *thoroughly*），
在此引申為「非常」。

4-2 We were *treated so well*.

這句話可加長為：We were treated so well by our
hosts. (主人招待我們很周到。) 也可說成：They were
so nice to us. (他們對我們很好。) 或 They were so kind
and polite. (他們很親切又有禮貌。)

4-3 It was *an unforgettable occasion*.

也可說成：It was a lifetime memory. (它是終生的
回憶。) 或 I will always remember it. (我將永遠記住。)
I will never forget it. (我將永遠忘不了。)

4-4　You *seem so excited*.

也可説成：You seem thrilled. (你似乎很興奮。) 或 You look psyched. (你看起來很興奮。)

thrilled〔θrɪld〕*adj.* 興奮的

psyched〔saɪkt〕*adj.* 興奮的【詳見「一口氣背會話」p.576】

4-5　*Fill me in*.

這句話的意思是「告訴我詳情。」【詳見「一口氣背會話」p.249】可加長爲：Please fill me in on all the details. (請告訴我所有的細節。) 也可説成：Tell me about it. (告訴我這件事。) (= *Let me know about it.*)

4-6　Tell me *what happened*.
　　　　　　　名詞子句

可加強語氣説成：Please tell me what happened to you. (請告訴我你發生了什麼事。)

4-7　You are *well-read*.

well-read〔'wɛl'rɛd〕*adj.* 博覽群書的；博學的

這是一句稱讚別人的話。可加強語氣説成：Everyone knows that you are well-read. (大家都知道你讀很多書。) 美國人也常説：You have read a lot. (你看了很多書。) (= *You have read many books.*) 或 You are knowledgeable. (你很有學問。)

【knowledgeable〔'nɑlɪdʒəbl̩〕*adj.* 知識豐富的】

也可說成：You are well-educated.（你受過良好的教育。）或 You are well-informed.（你見多識廣。）

【well-informed〔ˏwɛlɪnˈfɔrmd〕*adj.* 消息靈通的；見多識廣的】

4-8　You're interesting *to talk with*.

　　不定詞片語 to talk with 當副詞用，修飾形容詞 interesting。也可說成：You're a very interesting person to talk with.（和你談話很有趣。）talk with 可用 talk to 來代替。也可說成：I really enjoy talking with you.（我真的很喜歡和你談話。）

4-9　You're *always* *full of good ideas*.

　　可加長為：I think you're always full of good ideas.（我認為你總是有很多好點子。）或 You are always full of bright ideas.（你總是有很多奇妙的主意。）美國人也常說：You are smart.（你很聰明。）或 I think you are clever.（我認為你很聰明。）

　　中國人常把 full〔fʊl〕唸成 fool〔ful〕，方法是：長音儘量唸長，短音儘量唸短，碰到 /l/ 音時，舌尖要碰到上齒齦。

5.　Let's find out his arrival date.

Tom *is coming* next month.	湯姆下個月要來。
Let's *find out* his arrival date.　【2015 重慶】	我們查清楚他的到達日期吧。
We need to *book* a room for him.　【2015 重慶】	我們需要替他訂一個房間。
The meeting will *be held* in September. 【2015 重慶】	會議將在九月舉行。
It *is scheduled* to be in Shanghai.	會議安排在上海。
I don't know the exact date *for sure*. 【2015 重慶】	我不確定正確的日期。
I can't *attend* the meeting. 【2015 天津】	我無法參加會議。
I *will be teaching* a class at that time. 【2015 天津】	那個時候我要教課。
Let me know *what I miss*.	告訴我我沒聽到的事。

** ───────────

find out 發現；查明；弄清楚
book〔bʊk〕*v.* 預訂（= *reserve*）　　hold〔hold〕*v.* 舉行
schedule〔'skɛdʒʊl〕*v.* 安排；排定
exact〔ɪg'zækt〕*adj.* 確切的　*for sure* 一定；確實地
attend〔ə'tɛnd〕*v.* 參加　　miss〔mɪs〕*v.* 錯過

【背景説明】

　　　　朋友要來了，你要替他訂旅館，你該怎麼說？用背過的句子說出來才有信心，背得越多，你的英文越流利。不背的話，自己造句太危險了。

5-1　Tom *is coming* next month.

　　　come 是「來去動詞」，常用現在式或現在進行式表「未來」。也可說成：Tom plans to be here next month.（湯姆計劃下個月來這裡。）或 Tom hopes to visit here next month.（湯姆計劃下個月來這裡。）
（= *Tom is hoping to visit here next month.*）

5-2　Let's *find out* his arrival date.

　　find out 發現；查明；弄清楚（= *discover*）

　　　也可說成：Find out what date he is coming.（要查清楚他哪一天來。）或加長爲：Let's find out what his expected arrival date is.（我們要查清楚他預定到達的日期。）也可簡單地說：When is he coming?（他什麼時候來？）或 When will he be here?（他何時來這裡？）On what date does he arrive?（他哪一天到達？）

5-3　We need to *book* a room *for him*.

　　　book 在這裡作「預訂」解（= *reserve*）。這句話也可說成：We need to reserve a room for him.（我們需要替

他預訂一個房間。)(= *We need to make a reservation for him.*)　　reserve〔rɪˈzɝv〕*v.* 預訂
reservation〔ˌrɛzɚˈveʃən〕*n.* 預訂
make a reservation　預訂

5-4　The meeting will *be held* in September.

可簡單說成：The meeting will be in September.
（會議將在九月舉行。)(= *The meeting will take place in September.*)【take place　舉行；發生】

5-5　It *is scheduled* to be in Shanghai.

schedule 的主要意思是「時間表」，在這裡是動詞，作「安排；排定」解。

這句話也可說成：It is scheduled to be held in Shanghai.（安排在上海舉行。）或 It is planned to be held in Shanghai.（計劃在上海舉行。）

5-6　I don't know the exact date *for sure*.

也可說成：I'm unsure of the exact date.（我不確定正確的日期。）

for sure（一定；確實地）這個成語是由「介詞＋形容詞」所組成，類似的有：at large（逍遙法外）、in short（簡言之）等。【詳見「一口氣背會話」p.488】

> 在字典上，*for sure* 等於 for certain，但美國人較常用 *for sure*，例如：It wasn't me *for sure*.（當然不是我。）I wasn't there *for sure*.（我當然不在那裡。）There is no telling *for sure*.（當然沒有人知道。）

tell〔tɛl〕v. 知道
there is no telling 不可能知道（= *it is impossible to know*）

5-7 I can't *attend* the meeting.

也可說成：I can't be at the meeting.（我無法參加會議。）（= *I won't be there for the meeting.*）或 I'm unable to attend the meeting.（我無法參加會議。）

5-8 I *will be teaching* a class *at that time*.

可簡化為：I will be teaching a class then.（那個時候我要教課。）也可再簡化為：I will be teaching then.（那時候我要教書。）背完這句話，你就會用「未來進行式」了。

5-9 Let me know *what I miss*.
　　　　　　　名詞子句

可加長為：I want you to let me know what I miss.（我要你告訴我我沒聽到的事。）也可簡化為：Tell me what I miss.（告訴我我沒聽到的事。）可用 whatever 代替 what，說成：Let me know whatever I miss.（無論什麼我沒聽到的事都要讓我知道。）

6. *It cost an arm and a leg.*

We are *catching the first flight*.　【2015 北京】	我們要趕第一班飛機。
We need to *get up early*.　【2015 北京】	我們需要早起。
We must order a taxi *in advance*.　【2015 北京】	我們必須事先訂好計程車。
Don't *sit too long*.	不要坐太久。
Get up and *stretch your legs*.	起來動一動。
Good circulation is essential.	血液循環良好非常重要。
Be careful *with the camera*.　【2015 四川】	小心使用照相機。
Don't drop it.	不要掉下去。
It *cost an arm and a leg*.　【2015 四川】	它值很多錢。

** ───────────────

catch〔kætʃ〕*v.* 趕上　　flight〔flaɪt〕*n.* 班機

get up 起床；起身　　order〔ˈɔrdɚ〕*v.* 訂購

in advance 事先　　stretch〔strɛtʃ〕*v.* 伸展

stretch your legs 伸伸腿；起來動一動

circulation〔ˌsɝkjəˈleʃən〕*n.* (血液) 循環

essential〔əˈsɛnʃəl〕*adj.* 非常重要的

drop〔drɑp〕*v.* 掉落　　*cost an arm and a leg* 值很多錢

【背景説明】

要背英文短句，就要背好的句子，像 Don't sit too long. ，勸人在飛機上不要坐太久，接著説：Get up and stretch your legs. (起來動一動。) ，因爲血液循環很重要。

6-1 We are *catching the first flight*.

也可説成：We are *taking* the first flight. (我們要搭第一班飛機。) 可加長爲：We are going to catch the first flight in the morning. (我們要趕早上第一班飛機。)

這句話用現在進行式，表計劃未來的事情，又如：We are getting married in March. (我們要在三月結婚。)【詳見「文法寶典」p.342】

6-2 We need to *get up early*.

也可説成：　We need to *wake up* early. (我們需要早起。)
　　　　　= We need to *get out of bed* early.
　　　　　= We need to *rise (and shine)* early.

「起床」最常用的是 get up 和 wake up，第二常用的是 get out of bed，字面意思是「從床上出來」，引申爲「起床」。rise and shine 中的 rise 即是「起床」，如 He always rises early. (他總是早起。) 字典上有，但美國人口語中少説。rise and shine 字面意思是「起床發亮」，引申爲「起床」(= *get out of bed and start the day*)，是幽默的用語，有點像「起床幹活」。

6-3　We must order a taxi *in advance*.

也可說成：　We must *book* a taxi in advance.
（我們必須事先預約計程車。）

= We must *reserve* a taxi in advance.

in advance 事先（= *ahead of time*）

taxi（計程車）也可說成 cab 或 taxicab，但叫計程車時，只能用 *Hey, taxi!*（嘿，計程車！）。【詳見「一口氣背會話」p.237】

6-4　Don't *sit too long*.

也可說成：Don't sit for too long.（不要坐太久。）
或 Don't sit for too long a time.（一次不要坐太久。）
也可加長爲：You should not sit down for too long of a time.（你不應該一次坐太久。）

6-5　Get up and *stretch your legs*.
stretch 的意思是「伸展；伸懶腰」，*stretch your legs* 引申爲「起來動一動」。

這句話也可加長爲：You should get up and stretch your arms and legs frequently.（你應該常常站起來，活動一下手腳。）還可說成：Stand up and move around a lot.（站起來多走動走動。）Get on your feet and move often.（站起來多動一動。）Get out of your seat and stretch from time to time.（偶爾站起來伸伸懶腰。）

6-6　*Good circulation* is essential.
circulation 的主要意思是「循環」，在這裡是指「血

液循環」,「血液循環良好」稱作 good circulation,「血液循環不良」稱作 poor circulation。

這句話可加長為:Everyone knows that good circulation is essential for our health.（大家都知道,血液循環良好對我們的健康非常重要。）還可說成:It is very important to have good circulation.（血液循環良好非常重要。）或 Good blood flow is the key.（血液流通良好是關鍵。）

坐太久,造成血液循環不良,會有很多後遺症,容易得痔瘡、胃下垂、肥胖、肩頸腰酸背痛等,最好每 50 分鐘起來活動一分鐘以上。

6-7 Be careful *with the camera*.

可加長為:Please be careful with the camera. It's fragile.（請小心使用照相機。它很容易壞。）
【fragile〔ˈfrædʒəl〕*adj.* 易碎的;易損壞的】
也可說成:Don't break the camera.（不要把照相機弄壞。）或 Handle the camera with care.（小心拿照相機。）

6-8 Don't drop it.

也可說成:Don't let it drop.（不要讓它掉下來。）
（= *Don't let it fall.*）還可以說:Don't let it slip out of your hands.（不要讓它從你手中滑落。）

6-9 It *cost an arm and a leg*.

這句話字面意思是「它值一隻手臂和一條腿。」引申為「它值很多錢。」（= *It cost a lot of money.*）也可簡單說成:It cost a lot.「它很值錢。」或 It cost an awful lot.（它非常值錢。）或 It's very expensive.（它很貴。）
cost 用過去式的原因是根據上面兩句。

UNIT 6　7~9劇情簡介

【告訴朋友全球暖化的嚴重性】

7. *Global warming is a big issue.*
Global temperatures are
　　increasing.
Oceans are rising.

Is that so?
(是嗎？)

A small rise would be a disaster.
Just a centimeter would be
　　devastating.
·Future flooding is inevitable.

Oh my!
(噢！天啊！。)

We need to avoid this catastrophe.
Citizens must burn less carbon.
People must use clean energy
　　sources.

You're right.
(你說得對。)

* * *

【告訴朋友中國的快速發展】

8. *China is developing.*
The Chinese have achieved
　　great things.
They are trying to protect the
　　environment.

I see.
(我了解。)

"One Belt, One Road" is a new
    strategy.
The Silk Road Economic Belt is
    a key part.
China wants a bigger role in
    global affairs.

Tell me more.
(多告訴我一些。)

The AIIB will fund this project.
This bank was founded by China.
Membership includes many major
    countries.

Very interesting.
(非常有趣。)

* * *

【提到老闆、如何訂工作計畫】

9. ***The boss was elated.***
    She wanted better
        communications.
    She wanted all employees
        to enjoy their work.

She sounds like
    a good boss.
(她聽起來是個很好
    的老闆。)

Plan first.
Prepare second.
Finally, follow through.

So true!
(確實是！)

Excuse me, but I need your help.
I forgot to take my key.
I got locked out.

No problem
(沒問題。)

7. *Global warming is a big issue*.

Global warming is a big issue.	全球暖化是一項大問題。
Global temperatures are increasing. 【2015 重慶】	全球溫度逐漸升高。
Oceans are rising.	海洋正在上升。
A small rise would be *a disaster*.	上升一點點就是災難。
Just a centimeter would be *devastating*.	只要一公分就會造成毀滅。
Future flooding is *inevitable*.	未來，洪水無法避免。
We need to avoid this *catastrophe*.	我們需要避開這場大災難。
Citizens must *burn less carbon*.	人們必須減碳。
People must use *clean energy sources*.	人們必須使用淨潔能源。

＊＊

global warming 全球暖化　　issue〔ˈɪʃjʊ〕*n.* 問題；議題
temperature〔ˈtɛmprətʃə〕*n.* 溫度
disaster〔dɪzˈæstə〕*n.* 災難
centimeter〔ˈsɛntəˌmitə〕*n.* 公分　　flooding〔ˈflʌdɪŋ〕*n.* 洪水
inevitable〔ɪnˈɛvətəbl̩〕*adj.* 無法避免的
avoid〔əˈvɔɪd〕*v.* 避開
catastrophe〔kəˈtæstrəfɪ〕*n.* 大災難
citizen〔ˈsɪtəzn̩〕*n.* 公民；人民；人　　carbon〔ˈkɑrbən〕*n.* 碳

【背景說明】

全球暖化和節能減碳、使用淨潔能源，都是外國
人閒聊的話題，也是考試中常出現的主題。

7-1 *Global warming* is a big issue.

可說成：Global warming is a very serious problem.
（全球暖化是一個非常嚴重的問題。）(= *Global warming is
a very important matter.*)

7-2 *Global temperatures* are increasing.

可說成：Global temperatures are rising.（全球的溫
度逐漸升高。）或 The earth's weather is getting hotter.
（地球的天氣越來越熱。）可加長爲：Many scientific
studies show that global temperatures are increasing.
（許多科學研究顯示，全球的溫度正上升。）

7-3 Oceans are rising.

可加長爲：The world's oceans are rising because
of melting polar ice.（全世界海洋在上升，因爲極地的冰
在融化。）因爲全球暖化，南北極的冰融化，海洋上升，
造成洪水。

　　The earth is getting warmer.（地球逐漸暖化。）
　　Sea levels are rising.（海平面上升。）
　　(*sea level* = *ocean level*)
　　Melting polar ice results in flooding.
　　（極地的冰融化造成洪水。）
　　【melt〔mɛlt〕*v.* 融化　　polar〔'polɚ〕*adj.* 極地的】

7-4　A small rise would be *a disaster*.

可加強語氣說成：Just a small rise in ocean levels would be a disaster.（海平面只要上升一點點，就會造成災難。）因為這件事尚未發生，故用假設法助動詞 would。

也可簡單說成：A small increase would be a tragedy.（少少的上升就會造成悲劇。）

【ocean level　海平面　tragedy〔ˈtrædʒədɪ〕*n.* 悲劇】

7-5　Just a centimeter would be *devastating*.

devastate〔ˈdɛvəsˌtet〕*v.* 嚴重破壞；徹底摧毀，形容詞是 devastating「造成嚴重破壞的；毀滅性的」。

這句話可加長為：Just a centimeter rise in ocean levels would be devastating.（海平面只要上升一公分，就會造成毀滅。）

7-6　Future flooding is *inevitable*.

flooding〔ˈflʌdɪŋ〕*n.* 氾濫；洪水；淹水

也可說成：In the future, flooding is unavoidable.（未來洪水無法避免。）或 World flooding is certain to happen.（全世界洪水一定會發生。）

【unavoidable〔ˌʌnəˈvɔɪdəbḷ〕*adj.* 無法避免的】

7-7 We need to avoid this *catastrophe*.

catastrophe〔kə'tæstrəfɪ〕*n.* 大災難

　　這句話可加長爲：To survive, we need to avoid this coming catastrophe.（爲了生存，我們需要避開這個即將來臨的大災難。）也可說成：We must prevent this tragedy from happening.（我們必須阻止這種悲劇發生。）

coming〔'kʌmɪŋ〕*adj.* 即將來臨的

prevent…from 阻止…

7-8 Citizens must *burn less carbon*.

　　可加長爲：Citizens of the world must burn less carbon.（全世界的人都必須減碳。）(= *People of the world must burn less carbon.*)

7-9 People must use *clean energy sources*.

　　clean 主要意思是「乾淨的」，在此指「無污染的」，*clean energy sources*「無污染能源」，又稱「淨潔能源」(= *green energy*)，如 solar energy（太陽能）、wind energy（風能）等。

　　這句話可加長爲：To solve this problem, people must use clean energy sources.（爲了解決這個問題，人們必須使用無污染能源。）還可說成：All people need to start using green energy.（所有人都需要開始使用綠能。）

【green〔grin〕*adj.* 綠色的；環保的】

8. China is developing.

China is *developing*.	中國正在發展。
The Chinese have *achieved great things*.【2015 北京】	中國人已經有了很大的成就。
They are trying to *protect the environment*.【2015 北京】	他們正在努力保護環境。
"One Belt, One Road" is a new strategy.	「一帶一路」是新的策略。
The Silk Road Economic Belt is a key part.【2015 江蘇】	「絲路經濟帶」是關鍵部分。
China wants *a bigger role* in global affairs.	中國要在全球事務中，扮演較大的角色。
The AIIB will fund this project.	亞投行將會提供這項計劃資金。
This bank *was founded* by China.	這家銀行由中國創辦。
Membership includes many major countries.	會員包括許多主要國家。

** ──────────────

achieve〔əˋtʃiv〕*v.* 達成；成就
strategy〔ˋstrætədʒɪ〕*n.* 策略
Silk Road 絲路　　economic〔͵ikəˋnɑmɪk〕*adj.* 經濟的
affair〔əˋfɛr〕*n.* 事務　　fund〔fʌnd〕*v.* 提供資金
project〔ˋprɑdʒɛkt〕*n.* 計劃　　found〔faʊnd〕*v.* 創辦
membership〔ˋmɛmbɚ͵ʃɪp〕*n.* (全體) 會員

【背景説明】

中國已經變成全球矚目的焦點，「一帶一路」「絲路經濟帶」，和「亞投行」一定要弄清楚，和外國人談話才有話題。

8-1 China is *developing*.

這句話可加強語氣説成：China is developing rapidly. (中國正在迅速發展。) 句中 rapidly「迅速地」可改成 quickly「快速地」。再加強語氣，可説成：China is developing at a rapid pace. (中國現在正以快速的步伐向前發展。) 還可説成：

China is modernizing. (中國正在現代化。)
= China is growing. (中國正在成長。)
= China is advancing. (中國正在向前進。)
= China is progressing. (中國正在進步。)
= China is improving. (中國正在改進。)
= China is prospering. (中國越來越繁榮。)
= China is moving up. (中國正在向前進。)
(= *China is moving forward.*)

8-2 The Chinese have *achieved great things*.

可加長為：The Chinese have achieved great things in the past few decades. (過去幾十年來，中國人已經有了極大的成就。) 也可簡單説成：The Chinese have accomplished many things. (中國人完成很多事。) 句中 many things 可改成 a lot, accomplished 可改成 achieved 或 attained。

8-3　They are trying to ***protect the environment***.

　　　也可説成：They are trying to preserve their surroundings.（他們正在努力保護他們的環境。）

8-4　"***One Belt, One Road***" is a new strategy.

　　　「一帶一路」是指「絲綢之路經濟帶（一帶）」和「21世紀海上絲綢之路（一路）」，可簡稱爲 Belt and Road，縮寫爲 BAR。

　　　這句話也可説成：China's new plan is called "One Belt, One Road."（中國的新計劃稱作「一帶一路」。）

8-5　***The Silk Road Economic Belt*** is a key part.

　　　Silk Road Economic Belt「絲綢之路經濟帶」，目的在消化中國過剩的產能，並帶動西部的開發，簡稱爲 SREB，可説成：The SREB is a key part of China's new economic plan.（絲路經濟帶是中國新經濟計劃的關鍵部分。）It starts in Xi'an, passes through Urumuqi, Istanbul, and Moscow, and ends in Venice.（它開始於西安，經過烏魯木齊、伊斯坦堡、莫斯科，到威尼斯。）

8-6　China wants ***a bigger role*** in global affairs.

　　　可説成：China wants to play a bigger role in global affairs.（中國想要在全球事務中，扮演較大的角色。）
可簡化爲：China wants to be a world leader.（中國想要成爲世界的領導者。）

8-7 The AIIB will fund this project.

> 　　一般美國人會話中喜歡用縮寫，AIIB 指 Asian Infrastructure Investment Bank（亞洲基礎建設投資銀行），中文簡稱爲「亞投行」，總部設於中國北京，資本額爲 1,000 億美元，目的在於加強中國與亞洲國家間的合作，提供資金支持基礎建設。fund 這個字主要當名詞用，作「資金」解，在此是動詞，指「提供資金」（= *provide money for sth.*）。
>
> 　　這句話也可加長爲：The AIIB will provide most of the money for this project.（亞投行將提供這項計劃大部分的資金。）The AIIB will pay for this project.（亞投行將爲這項計劃提供資金。）

8-8 This bank *was founded* by China.

　　可加長爲：The AIIB was founded by China in 2014.（亞投行在 2014 年由中國創辦。）句中 founded 可用 established 來代替，還可説成：This bank was created by China.（這家銀行是由中國創建。）或 China set up this bank in 2014.（中國在 2014 年建立這家銀行。）

8-9 Membership includes many major countries.

　　可加長爲：Membership of the AIIB includes many major countries of the world.（亞投行的會員包括世界上許多主要國家。）可簡單地説：Many important countries are members.（許多重要國家都是會員。）或 Many countries are members of this bank.（許多國家都是這個銀行的會員。）

9. *The boss was elated.*

The boss was *elated*.	老板很高興。
She wanted better *communication*.	她想要更好的溝通。
She wanted all employees to enjoy their work.【2015 天津】	她要所有員工喜歡工作。
Plan first.	計劃第一。
Prepare second.	準備第二。
Finally, *follow through*.	最後，堅持到底。
Excuse me, *but* I need your help.	對不起，我需要你的幫助。
I forgot to *take my key*.	我忘記帶鑰匙。
I *got locked out*.【2015 四川】	我被鎖在外面。

**

elated〔ɪˈletɪd〕*adj.* 興高采烈的
communication〔kəˌmjunəˈkeʃən〕*n.* 溝通
employee〔ˌɛmplɔɪˈi〕*n.* 員工
follow through 貫徹到底
lock〔lɑk〕*n.* 鎖　*v.* 鎖住

【背景説明】

　　　當一個快樂的老板，就要讓員工喜歡他們的
工作，做任何事都要先計畫，再準備，最後要堅
持到底。

9-1　The boss was *elated*.

　　　elated〔ɪ'letɪd〕 adj. 興高采烈的，這個字的動詞 elate
〔ɪ'let〕 v. 使興高采烈，很少用，名詞是 elation〔ɪ'leʃən〕
n. 興高采烈。

　　　這個句子可加長爲：The boss was elated about the
company's success.（老板對公司的成功非常高興。）也可
説成：The boss was extremely happy.（老板非常高興。）
(= *The boss was delighted.*)

9-2　She wanted better *communications*.

　　　也可説成：She wanted better communication among
employees.（她想要員工之間有更良好的溝通。）或 She
hoped to improve relationships among workers.（她想
要改善員工之間的關係。）

9-3　She wanted all employees to enjoy their work.

　　　可加強語氣説成：She wanted all her employees
to thoroughly enjoy their work.（她想要她所有的員工
非常喜歡他們的工作。）

9-4　*Plan first*.

　　可加長為：To plan well is first.（好好計劃是第一。）
To plan well is the first thing to do.（好好計劃是第一個
要做的事。）To succeed, plan first.（要成功，先計劃。）
做任何事情，都要有好的計劃，美國人常說：First, have
a good plan.（首先，要有好的計劃。）或 First, plan
carefully.（首先，要小心計劃。）

9-5　*Prepare second*.

　　可加長為：To prepare carefully is the second thing
to do.（小心準備是第二個要做的事。）美國人常說：To
prepare thoroughly is a key to success..（準備充分是成
功的關鍵。）

9-6　Finally, *follow through*.
follow through　貫徹到底（ = *continue doing something
until it has been completed*）

　　這句話可加長為：Finally, you must follow the job
through to the end.（最後，你必須把工作貫徹到底。）還
可說成：Finally, complete the job.（最後，把工作完成。）
(= *Finally, finish the job*.）美國人常說：Don't leave
it half done.（做事不要做一半。）

9-7 *Excuse me*, *but* I need your help.

> Excuse me、I'm sorry、I beg your pardon 後可接
> *but*，也可省略，*but* 通常不翻譯，但不可用 *because* 代
> 替。
>
> 【比較】 Excuse me, *but* I need your help.【正，語氣較強】
> Excuse me, I need your help.【正，一般語氣】
> *Excuse me, because I need your help.*【誤】
>
> 可簡單地說：I need your help, please.（拜託，我
> 需要你的幫助。）或 Could you help me?（你能幫我嗎？）

9-8 I forgot to *take my key*.

> 可加長為：I forgot to take my gate key with me.
> （我忘記把大門鑰匙帶在身上。）也可說成：I don't have
> my key with me.（我身上沒有鑰匙。）或 I must have
> forgotten my key.（我一定是忘了鑰匙。）

9-9 I *got locked out*.

> 這句話源自 I got locked *out of my house*.（我被鎖
> 在房子外面。）也可說成：I locked myself out.（我把我
> 自己鎖在門外。）可接著說：I can't get in.（我進不去。）
> I can't open the lock.（我沒辦法開鎖。）I can't open
> the door.（我沒辦法開門。）

一口氣考試英語 Unit 6

※ 以三組爲一個單位較好背。

1. *Are you sure you can make it?*
   Don't just say it *to be nice*.
   Don't change your mind *at the last minute*. 【2015 重慶】

   Don't *miss the chance*. 【2015 重慶】
   This is your big opportunity.
   It may be years *before you get another one*. 【2015 重慶】

   I didn't invite her *on purpose*.
   　　【2015 江蘇】
   She's not a *social person*.
   She's a *wet blanket*. 【2015 江蘇】

2. She is *a shy person*. 【2015 北京】
   She is afraid to meet anyone.
   　　【2015 北京】
   She *puts a wall* between
   　　herself and others.

   Don't worry about *finding the location*. 【2015 北京】
   I will give you clear directions.
   　　【2015 北京】
   You'll have *no trouble getting there*. 【2015 北京】

   The party is in the park.
   It is near the main gate.
   Opposite is Starbucks.
   　　【2015 北京】

3. We have just *one more day to go*.
   　　【2015 四川】
   Tomorrow is *a big day*.
   I'm really *looking forward to* it.

   It's so noisy here. 【2015 浙江】
   I can't *hear myself think*. 【2015 浙江】
   It's *driving me crazy*.

   The park was *packed*. 【2015 北京】
   They enjoyed themselves *in the sunshine*. 【2015 北京】
   Everyone *had a blast*.

   　　　*　　*　　*

4. *We totally enjoyed the party*.
   　　【2015 北京】
   We were *treated* so well. 【2015 北京】
   It was *an unforgettable occasion*.

   You *seem so excited*. 【2015 天津】
   Fill me in.
   Tell me *what happened*.

   You are *well-read*.
   You're interesting *to talk with*.
   You're always *full of good ideas*.
   　　【2015 四川】

5. Tom *is coming* next month.
   Let's *find out* his arrival date.
   　　【2015 重慶】
   We need to *book* a room for him.
   　　【2015 重慶】

The meeting will *be held* in September. 【2015 重慶】
It *is scheduled* to be in Shanghai.
I don't know the exact date *for sure*. 【2015 重慶】

I can't *attend* the meeting.
【2015 天津】
I *will be teaching* a class at that time. 【2015 天津】
Let me know *what I miss*.

6. We are *catching the first flight*.
【2015 北京】
We need to *get up early*. 【2015 北京】
We must order a taxi *in advance*.
【2015 北京】

Don't *sit too long*.
Get up and *stretch your legs*.
Good circulation is essential.

Be careful *with the camera*.
【2015 四川】
Don't drop it.
It *cost an arm and a leg*. 【2015 四川】

*   *   *

7. *Global warming is a big issue*.
Global temperatures are increasing. 【2015 重慶】
Oceans are rising.

A small rise would be *a disaster*.
Just a centimeter would be *devastating*.
Future flooding is *inevitable*.

We need to avoid this *catastrophe*.
Citizens must *burn less carbon*.
People must use *clean energy sources*.

8. China is *developing*.
The Chinese have *achieved great things*. 【2015 北京】
They are trying to *protect the environment*. 【2015 北京】

"One Belt, One Road" is a new strategy.
The Silk Road Economic Belt is a key part. 【2015 江蘇】
China wants *a bigger role* in global affairs.

The AIIB will fund this project.
This bank *was founded* by China.
Membership includes many major countries.

9. The boss was *elated*.
She wanted better *communication*.
She wanted all employees to enjoy their work. 【2015 天津】

Plan first.
Prepare second.
Finally, *follow through*.

Excuse me, *but* I need your help.
I forgot to *take my key*.
I *got locked out*. 【2015 四川】

※ 可將這兩頁用手機拍下來背。

Mother held my arm. 這句話正確嗎？

　　美國人大多都不會寫文章，因為說的和寫的不一樣，我們所學的教科書，是美國人寫的，沒有生命，因為他們怕文法有錯。我常聽美國人說：*Got a minute? You need to hear this.* 編成會話課本，就變成：Have you got a minute? 或 Do you have a minute? 或 Are you free? 照課本這樣說的英文就不道地了。我們在「一口氣考試英語」中有：

> *Got a minute?*（你有空嗎？）
> *You need to hear this.*（你得聽聽這個。）
> *I have an interesting piece of information.*
> （我有一個有趣的消息。）

第三句話考試中常考，因為 information 很特殊，是不可數名詞，

> I have *an* information.【誤】
> I have information.【正】

不可數名詞要用單位名詞表數的觀念，要說成：

> I have a piece of information.（我有一個消息。）

> I have an interesting piece of information.

【形容詞必須加在單位名詞前】

這樣研究起來太辛苦了，可應付考試，卻不會應用在會話中。但是背完了上面三句話，會說話，也會考試。

　　有一位美籍教授 Laura Stewart，和我們工作 20 多年，對文法有深刻的了解，但我們給她校對：Stick with me, the best is yet to come. 她卻要把逗點改成分號，寫成：Stick with me; the best is yet to come. 其實，逗點沒有錯，就像 Trust me, you can make it. 一樣是慣用句。先有語言才有文法，不是每個句子都合乎文法規則，美國出版的教科書，都是這些有學問的人編寫的，跳過不合文法的句子，所編成的書本學起來就不生動，與日常生活格格不入，所以我們會話才會學不好。

　　用文法造句太可怕了，在字典上，equal 等於 be equal to，都當「等於」解，我們可以說：Money does not equal happiness.（錢不等於快樂。）卻不能說：*Money isn't equal to happiness.*（誤），那為什麼

Seven days $\begin{Bmatrix} \text{is equal to} \\ \text{equals} \end{Bmatrix}$ a week. 又可以呢？英文就這麼複雜！

equal（等於；相當於）和 be equal to（等於；和～一樣）有一點不同，卻差很遠，*Money isn't equal to happiness.*（誤）字面意思是「錢和快樂不一樣。」這個句子沒有意義，所以是錯誤的，在這裡，be equal to 等於 be the same as，造成句意不合理。

高雄的郭雅惠博士問我，action（行動）不是抽象名詞嗎？抽象名詞不是沒有複數形嗎？那爲什麼 "Actions speak louder than words."（行動勝於言辭。）中，Actions 是複數呢？英文一個字常有多個意思，在字典上註明 C，表示可數名詞，註明 U，表示不可數名詞，It's time for action.（是採取行動的時候了。）action 是抽象名詞，但在 Actions speak louder than words. 中，action 指「一個一個的行爲」，是可數名詞。你看，人類花那麼多工夫學英文，研究英文文法，都把它編到字典裡面去了，如此嚴謹的造句規則，無人學得會，無人學得完，所以，我們學英文的方法百年來都錯了。

最簡單的方法是背短句，學文法大規則，不懂的才去查，例如：Mother *held* me *by the arm*.（媽媽抓住我的手臂。）這種句子常考，因爲很特殊，文法規則是：「主詞＋動詞＋某人＋介詞＋the＋某人身體一部分」，這種句子就需要查文法書，但大家還是忽略了最基本的 "Mother held my arm."（媽媽抓住我的手臂。）也是正確的。和別人説話時，一邊想著文法規則，一邊造句，很難，又容易犯錯，背了下面三句話，你就立刻會説了。

Mother *held* me *by the arm*.（媽媽抓住我的手臂。）
She *patted* me *on the shoulder*.（她拍拍我的肩膀。）
She didn't want me to leave.（她不想要我離開。）

原先，「一口氣考試英語」的發明，是爲了同學考試，想不到，把考試題目用在生活英文中，你説出來的英文比美國人還好，**我們不只在學英文，我們在學説話，我們在學如何説流利、正確的英文**，同學們背完後，參加考試用得到，考試可以考高分，寫作文也用得到，每句話都正確，寫出來的文章一定是句句精彩。只要有事沒事每天背一背，英文就學好了，不是很輕鬆愉快嗎？

劉　毅

1.
Our work is done.
Now we can relax.
It's such a lovely day that everybody feels like going out.

our work is done
= Our job is done.
be done 完成
= be finished = be complete

A : B = C : D
A is to B {what / as} C is to D.

A之於 B 猶如 C之於 D。

It being Sunday, the theater will be crowded.
It won't be easy getting tickets.
Why don't we go on a weekday?

2.
I'm sorry I made you wait.
It couldn't be helped.
                avoided
A traffic jam prevented me from arriving on time.

prevent ~ from 阻止
= stop ~ from
= keep ~ from

It's such a lovely day that everybody feels like going out.

I don't read much.
Watching movies is like a kind of reading to me.
Reading is to the mind what exercise is to the body.
exercising X

Watching movies
Watching a movie
Seeing a movie   } is like…
Seeing movies (X)

It being Sunday,
= As it is Sunday

It won't be easy getting tickets.
= It won't be easy to get tickets.

on a weekday 在平日
= during the week

一般人說: The theater will be crowded on Sunday.
on a weekend 在周末 (= on the weekend)

I didn't sleep well.
I [tɔst] tossed and turned [tɜnd] all night.

The bed I slept in wasn't very comfortable.

toss and turn
翻來覆去睡不好
= be unable to sleep

I'm a responsible person.
I'm always on time.
As far as work is concerned,
  I always try to do my
  best.
= As far as { my work / my job } is concerned, ...
  as far as ... is concerned
  就~而言
= as for
= as to

Old habits die hard.
  舊習慣難改。
Old dogs cannot learn
  new tricks. 老狗變不了新把戲。
A bad habit, once formed,
  cannot be easily gotten
  rid of.

once formed 源自
once (it is) formed

I need you.
There is much to be done.
It is essential that you
  be here now.

It is { essential / necessary / important } that S +
  (should) + V原
  必要

一般人說 = You must be here
  now.

3. I'll be with you.
   I'll support you.
   As long as I live, I will
     not let you go hungry.
       挨餓

Are you still eating?
It's not good for you.
You cannot lose weight
  until you give up eating
  between meals,
    吃零食

主動: You must get rid of
       vt. 戒除
       a bad habit.
被動: A bad habit must be
       gotten rid of.
       vi.

4. Call me.
   Contact me.
   Should anything happen,
     let me know immediately.
   = If anything should
     happen, ...   原一

Your situation is awful.
Stick with me, the best
  is yet to come.
  和我在一起，好事終將到來。
All things considered, this
  is the safest policy.

Stick with me and the
  best is yet to come.
    終將
  [慣用句]

P.2

Trust me, you can make it.
[以後用的]

All things (being) considered
因為

從整體看來 [慣用語]

All things considered, we
did a good job.

5.
I don't want to be late.
Let's not take a regular
train. 普通車

Let's take an express 快車
train so that we can
get there earlier.

so that 為了 [表目的]
= in order that
= that

Oh, no, we missed it.
噢，糟糕，我們沒趕上車。

The train has left.
If we had arrived
earlier, we could have
caught the train.
[假設法過去式]

This isn't it.
We got lost somehow.

The place which we are
looking for is on the
main street.

This is it. 就是這裡。
This isn't it. 不是這個地方。
Somehow 不知道為什麼

6.
I'm going to try it.
I'm going to give it
a shot

whether you agree or
s
not will make no
difference.

give it a shot 試試看
= give it a try
= try it

Our letter to you was
returned.
Our phone call to you
went unanswered.
was
Please inform us of any
address change.

I understand why you
did it.
I'm not angry with you.
I don't blame you for
doing that.

P. 3

inform sb. of sth.
通知某人某事

blame sb. for sth.
責備某人某事

ask sb. for sth.
向某人要求事物

thank sb. for sth.

Thank your money. (x)
Thank you for your
money. (v)

do some shopping 去購物
= do one's shopping
= go shopping

Buy what you need
受 主詞

Don't buy what you
want.   受 主詞

I didn't buy anything
because I didn't see
what I needed.
受   主詞

7. Here is some good
advice.
Learn something new
every day.
Now that you are in
Taipei, you should
do some shopping.

now that 因為; 既然
= now
= since

Simple pleasures are the
best.
I'm a frugal person.
節儉的

Poor as I am, I live
雖然
happily.

Poor as I am, ···
= Although I am poor, ···

8. It's getting late.
Traffic will be light.
It's time we left now.

It's time
It's about time } + S + 過去式 V···
It's high time

是該···的時候了。

一般人說: We should go now

The weather can turn bad
in the blink of an eye.
Better safe than sorry.
[諺] 安全總比後悔為好。
I think we had better
carry an umbrella
in case it rains.

P. 4